SURVIVALS

Aspects of Industrial Archaeology
in Ontario

Dianne Newell and Ralph Greenhill

SURVIVALS

Aspects of Industrial Archaeology in Ontario

Dianne Newell and Ralph Greenhill

THE BOSTON MILLS PRESS

Canadian Cataloguing in Publication Data

Newell, Dianne Charlotte Elizabeth, 1943-
    Survivals : aspects of industrial archaeology
in Ontario
Bibliography: p.
Includes index.
ISBN 1-55046-000-5

1. Industrial archaeology — Ontario.   2. Ontario —
Industries — History.   I. Greenhill, Ralph,
1924-   . II. Title.

T23.05N48 1989   609'.713   C89-093549-1

Acknowledgments

Field work and the wide-ranging nature of our project required the help and co-operation of many individuals and institutions. We are especially grateful to the following: John M. Campbell and Heather M. Campbell (Gananoque Light & Power Ltd.), W. Glen Curnoe (London Room, London Public Libraries and Museums), Jane Foster (Lennox & Addington County Museum), John P. Good (Trent-Severn Waterway, Parks Canada), John Jeronimus (Regional Engineering, CN Toronto), Benjamin F.G. Kline, Jr. (Railroad Museum of Pennsylvania), Walter Lewis (Halton Hills Public Library), William H. Loos (Buffalo & Erie County Public Library), Robert W. Passfield (Historical Research Division, Parks Canada), Donna McGuire (Oil Museum of Canada, Oil Springs); Margo Teasdale (Heritage Branch, Ontario Ministry of Culture and Communications), the staff of the Baldwin Room, Metropolitan Toronto Library, and also Raymond F. Corley, Paul Craven, Henry W. Fischer, Ivan Harris, Charles W. Humphries, Robert G. Hill, Phil Morningstar, Nick & Helma Mika, Larry Pfaff, Wanda Pratt, Gordon Ridout, David Rollinson, Susan M. Sawyer, and Edward Storey.

Individual essays were read by Paul J. Allsop (Gooderham & Worts Ltd.), Martin H. Bosch, Charles Fairbank, Terry Mundell, Charles Nixon, and Douglas N. Wilson (CN Sarnia); their expert criticisms improved our text. Special mention must be made of the contributions of Stephen A. Otto, who kept our project in mind when doing his own research on Gooderham & Worts and other sites in Ontario, and John Denison, publisher of The Boston Mills Press, whose help with this project went well beyond that which an author would normally expect. We also appreciate the financial support provided by a number of agencies: the Massey Foundation (a grant to complete the photography), the Arts Council of Ontario, the Ontario Heritage Foundation, the Social Sciences & Humanities Research Council of Canada, and UBC Faculty of Arts.

Finally, this book is dedicated to a friend and colleague, Robert M. Vogel, Smithsonian Institution, who paved the way for industrial archaeology in North America.

Contents

Introduction

The transformation of industry and engineering over the past 200 years has affected every aspect of modern life. This book is concerned with examining the surviving evidence of that transformation in an approach to history known as 'industrial archaeology'. Besides using the conventional archival and library sources available to historians, industrial archaeologists study sites, structures, equipment, and processes, even the landscape itself.

When we think of old industrial structures, we usually think of derelict factories, but they represent only one type of industrial archaeological site. Some industrial archaeological remains are buried, and as such they require the use of remote sensing techniques, such as aerial photography[1] or excavation.[2] Excavation is especially appropriate when a buried site is threatened with destruction. In the early 1980s Parks Canada excavated the remains of two large mills on the site of the future National Museum of Civilization in Hull, Quebec: a steam-powered sawmill belonging to Wright, Batson, et Currier (operated 1868 to 1878) and a pulp mill of the E.B. Eddy Company (operated 1898 to 1972). So many excellent examples of industrial archaeology remain above ground, however, that excavation is seldom undertaken.

Surprisingly, a number of industrial archaeological sites contain standing structures and equipment which have changed little since originally built and operated. A few of them still function for their original purpose, while others have been preserved as historic sites or museums. But these are the exceptions. As a rule, most sites and structures have undergone extensive alterations throughout their history, and many have been adapted for new uses — often more than once. The changes can be studied and interpreted only by carefully recording and documenting the physical remains[3] and tracking down the appropriate people and documents.

Industrial archaeology began around 1960 in Britain, where the Industrial Revolution began. North Americans founded the world's first society for industrial archaeology in Washington, D.C., in 1971. Interest has since spread to many countries and regions of the world. An international organization (The International Committee for the Conservation of the Industrial Heritage) has been formed, with representatives from over 30 countries, including Canada. Canada has no national organization of its own (the Society for Industrial Archeology has always functioned as a North American organization), but both Ontario (Ontario Society for Industrial Archaeology) and Quebec

1 See Dianne Newell, 'Surveying Historic Industrial Tidewater Sites: The Case of the B.C. Salmon Canning Industry,' *IA: The Journal of the Society for Industrial Archaeology* [IA] 13, 1 (1987): 1-16.

2 David Newlands excavated several pottery sites in the southwestern region and a glass works at Napanee for the Royal Ontario Museum. For a list of his reports on pottery excavations, see David Newlands, *Early Ontario Potters: Their Craft and Trade* (Toronto, 1979), select bibliography.

3 See H.J. McKee, compiler, *Recording Historic Buildings* (Washington, D.C., 1970), pp. 138-147.

(Association québecoise pour le patrimonie industriel) have recently formed regional societies. In spite of this rather slow beginning, there is every indication of a growing public interest in the industrial and engineering heritage in this country.

The collection of essays that follows is intended to provide the beginnings of an introduction to industrial archaeology in Canada. It focuses on some aspects of the industrial heritage in southern Ontario, where during the nineteenth century Canadian manufacturing and engineering became concentrated. While the topics illustrate the variety and significance of the industrial heritage in the province, we are not attempting to provide a conventional 'IA' guide to sites, nor are we claiming any sort of comprehensive survey of the various types of sites, industries, or regions. We have deliberately rejected any such plans in favour of a series of in-depth essays. These essays are based on field observation and historical research, and include historic illustrations and modern photographs by Ralph Greenhill.

Ontario's industrial era began before Confederation, in the 1840s and 1850s, when the beginnings of steam-powered factories and transport systems ushered in a new era of manufacturing, urban life, and long-distance, year-round transportation. In these decades Ontario industry was, of course, powered largely by waterwheels and, mainly for that reason, geographically scattered, since local sources of water power and of raw materials determined the location of mills and factories.[4] Of the major industrial cities in Ontario by 1860, however, only Ottawa had substantial water power potential. Toronto and London had almost none, and Hamilton and Kingston had none at all. Stationary steam technology was introduced on a limited basis in these and smaller industrial cities such as Brantford, Guelph, Oshawa, Peterborough, St. Catharines, Sarnia, and Windsor. Steam engines powered not only industry but also the pumping stations of the municipal water systems established in most major Canadian cities before 1870. It is interesting that the earliest supply and sewage systems were intended more for industrial than domestic use.[5]

Typically, the introduction of stationary steam technology is seen as having contributed to increasing geographical concentration — urbanization — because it freed early industrial entrepreneurs from a dependency on sites

4 Discussed in Ian M. Drummond, *Progress Without Planning: The Economic History of Ontario from Confederation to the Second World War* (Toronto, 1987), pp. 134-35 and 166-84.
5 See Nelson M. Blake, *Water for the Cities: A History of the Urban Water Supply Problem in the United States* (Syracuse, 1956).

with water power potential. But because it was geographically unlimited, steam technology also provided a dispersive capacity, enabling the growth of forestry, mining, quarrying, and petroleum drilling and pumping.[6] Without steam power, the owners of the pioneer oil fields of southwestern Ontario, discovered in 1858, would have been unable to work their properties on a commercial basis.

The most dramatic transformation of the industrial era occurred during the period from Confederation to World War I. This was the period of Ontario's 'industrial revolution',[7] characterized by rapid urban growth, industrial expansion (both in scale, number, and range of operations),[8] and a transformation of the transport system and of the energy base. These changes became embedded in the landscape and still can be seen today. The legacies of the competitive expansion among the railway and canal networks throughout central Canada, for example, include the Peterborough Lift Lock on the Trent Canal, the Canadian Northern Railway's Scherzer Rolling Lift Bridge across the Rideau Canal at Smiths Falls, the Grand Trunk Railway's St. Clair Tunnel, and the Whirlpool Rapids Bridge across the Niagara River.

Hydroelectricity (electric lighting beginning in the 1880s and then power generation and the introduction of the individual electric motor) reduced Ontario's dependency on imported coal and local supplies of cordwood to fuel steam technology. In the case of the Trent and Rideau canals, hydroelectricity and canal development were interconnected because of the water control function of these particular canals. Both canals skirted the southern extension of the Canadian Shield. With improvements to the navigation and water control systems on both the Rideau and Trent waterways early this century, private and municipal electrical plants replaced many of the small hydraulic mills that had sprung up along the routes. On the Trent waterway, Ontario Hydro eventually acquired most of the generating stations and built others itself.[9] The only station on the Rideau waterway ever to be owned and operated by Ontario Hydro is in the old industrial town of Merrickville. (Private interests built the Merrickville electric plant in 1915; Ontario Hydro acquired it in 1949.) Ontario Hydro had been formed in 1906 as a public power distribution agency and began generating its own electricity in 1914. It was the first provincially owned electric utility in Canada and it has placed Canada in the forefront of hydroelectric pioneering nations. Because of the attention

6 Dianne Newell, *Technology on the Frontier: Mining in Old Ontario* (Vancouver, 1986), pp. 5, 18-38.

7 Drummond, *Economic History of Ontario*, p. 22.

8 See ibid., p. 401, table 7-9, 'Ontario's 15 Largest Industries . . . 1870 and 1910;' and W.G. Dean, ed., *Economic Atlas of Ontario* (Toronto, 1969), plate 31, 'Manufacturing Employment by County, 1871-1961.'

9 Mark Fram, *Ontario Hydro: Ontario Heritage: A Study of Strategies for the Conservation of the Heritage of Ontario Hydro* (Toronto, 1980), pp. 42-43 and 60-61.

given to Ontario Hydro, historians have tended to overlook the role of the privately operated hydroelectric companies which were so common in Ontario until World War II.

New technology often proved uneconomical or impractical. Thus, in spite of the availability of steam engines, it was often possible and practical to continue using water power. New types of waterwheels in the form of turbines were introduced around mid-century, so that water power actually reached its most mature level of development only during the late stages of the steam age in the 1880s and 1890s. The performance of a power system cannot be judged by the source of power alone, of course, but must also be judged by the delivery of the power to the machines or machinery to be driven. New systems of power transmission in the form of belt- or rope-driven line shafting made water- and steam-powered factories economical. Likewise, in spite of the availability of electric power beginning in the 1890s, the steam engine remained an important power source in industries using thermal processes (thus requiring steam heat), such as distilling and soap manufacturing, well into the present century. Sooner or later, individual motors (electric or sometimes gas) replaced the steam engines. The essays on belt and line-shafting transmission of power and on the Ontario oil fields address this all too often neglected question of the persistence of old techniques in the face of new advances.

Contrary to conventional wisdom, quality was a characteristic of Canadian industry and engineering. Canada was not an industrial or engineering backwater even in the colonial period. Indeed, half the essays in this volume deal with major accomplishments which occurred before Confederation. These early projects were not simply conceived externally, nor were they executed only by imported experts and financed only by foreign capital. Many were undertaken by people who grew up in this country and who reached outside for models, new technologies, ideas, and practices. Even after 1870, Canadian engineering firms and engineers continued to look to other countries for techniques and materials. They investigated the state of the art in the United States and abroad, then adapted and improved the imported techniques to suit Canadian needs and resources. This often occurred with the major publicly funded undertakings, such as the Peterborough Lift Lock project in the 1890s.

Privately financed development was equally significant and local entrepreneurs equally innovative. Britain financed and managed the Grand Trunk Railway, but Canadian engineers, subcontractors, and labour executed much of the best work. The Gooderham and Worts families were not only innovative in their distilling and malting business, but were heavily involved in running banks and financing narrow-gauge railways tapping Toronto's economic hinterland during the second half of the nineteenth century. In the first decade of the twentieth century, Toronto capital financed a major development line: the Canadian Northern Railway.

Canadian foundries and engineering firms, such as the Dominion Bridge Company of Lachine, Quebec, and the Gartshore and Bertram foundries in Dundas, made indispensable contributions too. Ontario had a dynamic foundry and machine-manufacturing industry. In the early years Ontario foundrymen often had no choice but to import materials and large or specialized structural members in order to fulfill their contracts. When Gartshore's large Dundas foundry[10] supplied the magnificent pumping engines for the Hamilton Water Works in the 1850s, it imported some of the larger parts for the great engines, the design of which was mostly British. But this of course changed over time. Although mistaken for an American design, the twin tunnel shields for excavating the St. Clair Tunnel in the 1890s were in fact designed by the Canadian-born engineer Joseph Hobson, and manufactured wholly by the Hamilton Tool & Bridge Company.

Ontario companies and government officials often imported engineers as consultants, arbitrators in awarding engineering contracts, and supervisors. In the early years British and American engineers designed several major engineering works, such as the Rideau Canal and the Niagara Railway Suspension Bridge. Yet, as indicated, the imported engineers always worked in conjunction with Canadian contractors and workmen. Moreover, Canadian-born engineers were gaining experience in Britain and the United States which they could then apply to challenging Canadian construction projects such as the Grand Trunk Railway.

The careers of distinguished Canadian engineers of the nineteenth century were unavoidably a mixture of politics and engineering, since in their day 'most big projects were public works in which the key jobs were political appointments.'[11] The Board of Works (after 1846 the Department of Public Works), headed by Hamilton H. Killaly, built and maintained many of the

10 Established in 1838 by the partnership of John Gartshore and James B. Ewart.
11 H.V. Nelles, 'Samuel Keefer,' *Dictionary of Canadian Biography*, Vol. XI (Toronto, 1982), p. 463.

province's roads and bridges, looked after timber slides, harbours, lighthouses, and canals (the Dominion government was in charge of navigable waterways and, unlike in the United States, all canal works were publicly operated projects). The department completed the St. Lawrence canal system in the 1840s, and by the 1850s oversaw the planning and construction of the provincial railway system.

Public works projects provided important training grounds for home-grown engineers such as Walter Shanly. He and his brother Francis had become neighbours of H.H. Killaly after their family had emigrated from Ireland in 1836. Four years later Walter Shanly became Killaly's engineering protégé as a young assistant on construction of the Beauharnois Canal. The first engineering employment for Francis Shanly was on the surveys for the Great Western Railway in 1846. The brothers worked together on construction of the Toronto to Sarnia section of the Grand Trunk Railway, and from 1858 to 1862 Walter was the railway's general manager. In 1868 the brothers worked together again when they took over the construction of the first major tunnelling work in the United States: the Hoosac Tunnel in Massachusetts.

A second pair of brothers, both engineers, were Samuel and Thomas Coltrin Keefer. Their father, George Keefer, was first president of the Welland Canal Company, chartered in 1824. Soon after leaving Upper Canada College, Samuel Keefer was employed in various positions on public works in the Canadas. When the upper and lower provinces were united in 1841, he was appointed engineer of the newly established Board of Works. It was in this position that in 1843-44 he designed and constructed the first suspension bridge in Canada, spanning the Ottawa River at the Chaudière Falls. This was the second major wire-cable suspension bridge to be built in North America, preceded only by Charles Ellet's Fairmount Bridge opened in 1842 over the Schuylkill at Philadelphia. More than twenty years later, in 1867-68, when in private practice, he designed and constructed the Niagara Falls & Clifton Suspension Bridge, the first bridge to be built just below the Falls. When opened in 1869 its span of 1,268 feet made it the longest single span in the world, until the completion of the Brooklyn Bridge fourteen years later.

Thomas Coltrin Keefer comes up directly and indirectly in several of the essays in this volume. He was the celebrated hydraulic engineer who designed and supervised construction of Hamilton's municipal waterworks and those in

Montreal and Ottawa, and was the consulting engineer on the water supply systems for other major cities. He was a founder and in 1888 first president of the Canadian Society of Civil Engineers; the following year he was elected president of the American Society of Civil Engineers. His presidential address to the Royal Society of Canada in 1899 promoted a major technological breakthrough that would launch a new industrial era in Ontario and elsewhere in Canada: hydroelectricity.

Most of the sites discussed in this book, important as they are, have received little attention in published histories. As a result, there were few reliable secondary sources to consult. The Peterborough Lift Lock is a notable exception, and the recent book of essays produced by the Friends of the Trent-Severn Waterway should serve as a model.[12] Over the years, some sites have been designated as having national, provincial, or municipal historic value, which means that bodies such as Parks Canada and the Ontario Heritage Foundation will have produced manuscripts and background reports on them. (Certainly not all important sites — the Gooderham & Worts distillery operation, for example — have received recognition from government heritage agencies. It is clear from this collection of essays that private, not public, initiative is essential if engineering and industrial sites are to survive.) On the other hand, there are useful contemporary records, particularly published government records, such as the annual reports of the Department of Transport and the many commissions of inquiry into canals, railways, hydroelectricity, and natural resource development. We found, too, that many of our sites had been the subject of at least one feature-length article in a leading engineering journal, illustrated magazine, or newspaper of the day. Engineering and industry were of interest to both professionals and the public alike. Furthermore, fires, accidents, and new construction or equipment updating at industrial and engineering sites usually resulted in a local newspaper story.

Collections of historic maps, drawings, photographs, and trade catalogues supplement the written record. The Royal Engineers and contemporary military topographers, for example, generated hundreds of maps and drawings showing construction features for the Rideau Canal, and amateur artists who worked on the canal produced many sketches and watercolour views of particular sections of it.[13] One of the best-known and most interesting of the

12 Jean Murray Cole, ed., *The Peterborough Hydraulic Lift Lock* (Peterborough, 1987).
13 See Robert W. Passfield, *Building the Rideau Canal: A Pictorial History* (Toronto, 1982), pp. 7-8.

Rideau Canal artists was Thomas Burrowes, an amateur topographic artist who joined Lieutenant-Colonel By's staff in 1826 as a clerk-of-the-works. During construction of the canal and afterwards, Burrowes produced a series of about 60 watercolour sketches of the canal and nearby towns, which include several views of the Jones Falls dam under construction.

For private manufacturing concerns, the written record usually is so thin that maps, plans, and illustrations become essential research tools. As is typical for most old manufacturing businesses, no early company records survive for Gooderham & Worts Ltd., though most of the Gooderham & Worts buildings constructed in 1859 and later do. Both the distillery and its location, however, were prominent enough in the city to inspire artists and journalists to document them. Last and most important, old fire insurance plans of the site and its larger context for various key years in its history have survived.

Industrial archaeologists have long appreciated the value of insurance surveys as historical documents for site-specific investigations of manufacturing plants.[14] Because fire insurance plans were made in a 'high age' of industrialization, and because the companies updated them as changes occurred, the plans present a unique record of changes to industrial buildings and processes over time.[15] Insurance maps exist for entire cities as single-sheet plans or complete atlases, and as site surveys for individual industrial properties.

Various incendiary features — the highly inflammable nature of the materials worked in the manufacturing process, wood frame construction, sources of heat and light, the explosive nature of steam engines and boilers, and the heat produced from power transmission using belts and shafting — made industrial properties special fire risks. The great fire at Gooderham & Worts distillery in October 1869 is an excellent case in point. At six o'clock in the evening, a small cask of benzine in the fermenting rooms of the distillery burst and set fire to the basement of the building. Within a few moments the flames had spread along the floor and up the walls. The two large ventilators on the east and west ends of the building served effectively, though unintentionally, as draft holes to intensify the fire. As the fire advanced, the spirits caught flame, spewed out the doorways, and for a time threatened to destroy the rest of the site. A wooden fence caught fire, then a pile of lumber. Ninety minutes after it broke out, the fire in the distillery was completely out of

14 G.T. Bloomfield, 'Canadian Fire Insurance Plans and Industrial Archeology,' *IA* 8, 1 (1982): 67-80; and Helena Wright, 'Insurance Mapping and Industrial Archeology,' *IA* 9, 1 (1983): 1-18.

15 Bloomfield, 'Canadian Fire Insurance Plans,' p. 67.

control. Because the architect had designed the factory to be of 'slow burn' construction, it took a long time to destroy it. Also, there was a very large quantity of grain in the mill which, as the floors gave way, fell to the ground first and remained a mass of red heat for hours.[16] In this instance, the walls remained standing and the structure was rebuilt.

Not all industrial enterprises were as outstanding as the Gooderham & Worts distillery. For a more marginal industrial operation or setting, a major fire would most likely have meant the end of the business. Researching the history of most industrial sites requires a heavy reliance on local inquiry. This includes visits to local libraries and museums, for they often will have small archival collections in addition to their collections of books and artifacts. Local newspapers sometimes run stories on old industries and engineering structures in the area, but as these are often full of contradictions, errors, and omissions, they must be used with great caution. A statement in an article on Petrolia's new historic exhibit on the oil industry which appeared in the *London Free Press* in 1980 provides an excellent example of the problem: 'By inventing the rig and jerker rod system (in 1903), Imperial Oil's founding [Frederick A.] Fitzgerald saved the oil industry when the wells began to give out around the turn of the century.'[17] It is true that Fitzgerald commissioned the rig, but it did not 'save' the oil industry nor did he invent the jerker rod system of power transmission. The jerker system had been used in the Ontario oil fields since about 1863, and its introduction had nothing to do with either Fitzgerald or Imperial Oil. Unfortunately, the reporter probably picked up the information from a well-intentioned but misinformed local source.

Despite some problems, nothing quite replaces contacts with owners, managers, workers, and neighbours, and visits to the site itself for acquiring special insights and unique information. Blair McFarlane, who lived at the Hamilton pumping station at the turn of the century when his father ran the Gartshore pumping engines there, wrote informally about his childhood memories of the pumphouse. Besides containing important technical information, his letter provides some interesting social commentary: 'I know what it feels like to ride the walking beams or to sit on your front porch (300 ft. away) on a balmy summer evening and hear those two old engines thumping away in the dark. A few kerosene lamps hanging around gave about as much illumination as a fist full of fireflies. [The engines] were very loyal soldiers.'[18]

16 Toronto *Globe*, 27 October 1869.
17 *London Free Press*, 21 June 1980.
18 Private correspondence, Blair A. McFarlane (Livonia, N.Y.) to Dianne Newell, 11 September 1975.

Sometimes when researching the past it is easy to forget that history is a continuing process. Between our initial visit to the sites in 1978 and 1979 and a return visit in 1987, major changes had already occurred — some of them quite dramatic. Within months of our first visit to photograph the Scherzer Bridge at Smiths Falls, the railway company had permanently abandoned the line, and, although locals saved the bridge by having it declared of national historic significance, it no longer operates. The London Soap Company plant burned to the ground in 1985. The Oil Well Supply Co. Ltd. replaced its old belt-driven equipment with modern automatic electrically operated machinery only a few years ago. Fittings Ltd. in Oshawa closed its doors permanently just days before we arrived for our return visit in June 1987. As this book goes to press, the new owners of the most historic distillery complex in North America, Gooderham & Worts Ltd., Toronto, are developing plans for that site which could permanently change (or perhaps preserve) its character. The loss of some of our original choices led us to find others of which we had previously been unaware: Mundell's water-powered, belt-driven planing mill in Erin, and the old Guelph Soap Co. works.

The purpose of this collection of case studies is not to romanticize the past but to promote a new way of looking at the human landscape around us, and to increase awareness of its historical significance. Many interesting Canadian industrial and engineering sites survive relatively intact and still in use. What follows is a sample of our personal favourites in southern Ontario.

I

The Rideau Canal

The Rideau Canal is the only canal dating from the great North American canal-building era of the early nineteenth century that remains operational with most of its original structures intact. It is of national historical interest not only because of its original construction history, but also because of the later technological developments affecting the system. Of special note is the essential water control function of the original system that has contributed to its long-term survival as a navigation channel. Built originally for military strategic purposes, the canal has served as an immigration route, as a local trade and forwarding artery, regional and local source of hydraulic power, and most recently as a national recreational area.

The canal, actually a canalized waterway, was built following the War of 1812 to provide a secure interior water route for moving troops and military supplies from the ocean ports of Quebec and Montreal to Kingston should another war with the United States occur. The Imperial government built the canal at its own expense and regular troops of that government maintained it until it was transferred to the Province of Canada in 1856. Work on the canal began in 1826 and finished six years later. In charge of the project was an Englishman, Lieutenant-Colonel John By, who with a dozen young Royal Engineers designed and supervised the works. Contracts for the excavation and masonry work at various points along the route were let to a handful of civilians, and hundreds of canal workers were recruited from Ireland, Lower Canada, and elsewhere. Building canals was, of course, not new in North America, but Col. By built locks and control dams on an unprecedented scale.[1] He foresaw the commercial potential and strongly advocated locks large enough for steamers. Thus, when completed in 1832, the 123-mile canal was a major steamboat system of 52 dams and embankments and 47 large masonry locks with a total lift of 437 feet. Approximately 18 miles of the total length of this route linking the Ottawa and St. Lawrence River systems are an artificial waterway. The remainder comprises the natural course of the Rideau and Cataraqui rivers and the extensive chain of lakes which form the central part of the system.

From the beginning of the canal's operation in 1832, the military traffic on it was light compared with the commercial traffic. Log rafts, barges, and steamers (first paddle steamers, then, by the 1840s, propeller-driven) for moving large bulk cargo such as farm produce, logs, lumber, coal, and the

1 Robert Legget, *Rideau Waterway*, second edition (Toronto, 1986), p. 16.

products of local mines plied the system.[2] Yet the navigation tolls collected on the canal seldom repaid the cost of operating and maintaining it, and by the 1850s the Imperial government was anxious to unload it. Only by promising to throw in the extensive canal lands, however, was the British Department of Ordnance able to persuade the Province of Canada to assume responsibility for the canal in 1856.[3] (The Department of Public Works took it over until the creation of the Dominion of Canada in 1867, when it fell under the jurisdiction of the Dominion Department of Public Works, then the Department of Railways and Canals (which in the 1930s became the Department of Transport), where it remained until it was declared a national Heritage Canal in 1972.

The Rideau Canal was to some extent responsible for the steady development of small towns and industries along its shores. This occurred not only, or even mainly, because of the cheap transport system the canal provided, but because of the water supply and water power it offered. The Rideau River basin extended for 1,500 square miles; together these two systems allowed an impounding of 255,000 acre feet of water.[4] Once in the hands of the Dominion government, the canal's hydraulic potential was heavily exploited; navigation continued to have top priority but the water not being used for locks could be used for water mills. The Dominion government made a concentrated effort to develop income through the leasing of water rights to local grist mill, sawmill, flour mill, and shingle mill operations.

During the nineteenth century water mills were built right at the locks and dams, though, as already stated, such developments were heavily regulated in order to preserve the integrated, artificial hydraulic unit that Col. By had carefully created. By and his engineers had designed dams and embankments to serve several different purposes. The first and most important of these was to create a suitable depth for navigation by increasing the general draft in parts of the canal and flooding out rapids upstream from the dam. Dams were built also on side streams, where it was necessary to regulate the seasonal flows, especially to control the potentially destructive freshets that flooded through the system each spring. The dams and sluices proved ultimately so successful for flood control in the region that proposals to dismantle the system in the 1930s were dropped.[5]

The most stunning example of an original masonry dam on the waterway is at Jones Falls, located 27 miles above Kingston at the junction of Sand and

2 See Edward Forbes Bush, *Commercial Navigation on the Rideau Canal, 1832-1961*. History and Archaeology No. 54 (Ottawa, 1981).
3 William D. Naftel, *The Rideau Waterway*, SIA Occasional Publications No. 1 (Washington, D.C., 1973), p. 11.
4 Brian S. Osborne and Donald Swainson, assisted by Susan Code, 'Dividing the Waters: A Preliminary Overview of Water Management on the Rideau, 1832-1972.' Parks Canada, Microfiche Report Series No. 179 (1985), pp. 96-97.
5 Naftel, *The Rideau Waterway*, p. 8.

Whitefish lakes. Here, a 1½-mile-long set of rapids fell 60 feet — the largest drop between Ottawa and Kingston. The stone masons and labourers under contract with John Redpath of Montreal built a spectacular stone gravity-arch dam rising 62 feet above the bottom of the narrow rocky ravine which it spans (plate 1-2). Built with sandstone key-work in rear, a mass of earth and rubble in front, and clay puddle between the two (plate 1-1), the dam measures 350 feet along its crest, which curves to a radius of 175 feet.[6] The blocks, which measure 6 feet by 4 feet and 18 inches thick, are arranged in vertical rather than horizontal courses. Forty masons and upwards of two hundred Irish and French Canadian labourers worked on the dam, turning basin, and the four locks at the site from 1827 to 1832, battling the effects of disease, heavy labour, and loneliness in this isolated, swampy area. The hand-hewn stone had to be drawn from two special quarries near Elgin, 6 miles from the site; the huge amounts of clay puddle required for the core wall of the dam had also to be transported to the site. The final product was a dam more than double the height of any stone-arch dam built in North America at that time.

The Jones Falls dam, referred to locally simply as the horseshoe dam, remains today virtually as constructed (plate 1-3), in perfect condition and maintenance free. The crest of earthwork became a local roadway which crossed the dam, though recently it has been permanently closed to road traffic. In the vicinity of the old temporary spillway opening on the south side of the dam, used during its construction, the openings for three wood-stave penstocks were cut through the solid stone masonry. These penstocks feed water under the 60-foot head created by the dam to a small concrete generating station constructed 1946-50 at the lower end of what is left of the gorge (plate 1-4).

An almost identical dam, the 40-foot-high, 360-foot-long Ascutney Gravity-Arch Mill Dam, was built only a few years later, in 1834, at Windsor, Vermont, by a group of local businessmen.[7] As tempting as it is to speculate about a possible connection between the two projects, none has been established. The purpose of the Vermont dam was to increase the utility of the local water-power sites along the stream and to provide increased power at the dam site. Being a local commercial undertaking, the masonry work on the Ascutney is not as fine as at Jones Falls, but certainly a high level of engineering skill is evident. With its ratio of base width to height of 0.90, the ideal standard proportion to this day, the Ascutney is a true gravity-arch dam.[8] (The

6 Great Britain, Corps of Royal Engineers, *Papers on the Subjects Connected with the Duties of the Corps of Royal Engineers* [*Papers of the Rideau Canal*] (London, 1837), pp. 120-21; and Robert Legget, 'The Jones Falls Dam on the Rideau Canal, Ontario, Canada,' *Transactions of the Newcomen Society* 31 (1959): 211.
7 Edwin A. Battison, 'Ascutney Gravity-Arch Mill Dam,' *IA: The Journal of the Society for Industrial Archaeology* 1, 1 (1975): 53.
8 Ibid.

downstream face of the Jones Falls dam is arched in plan and concave in profile, and thus it appears to be a true arched dam. Yet the ratio is only 0.44, which falls well short of the minimum acceptable ratio for a gravity dam, and this probably explains why the Royal Engineers at Jones Falls designed a supplemental earth dam behind the stone dam.[9] Like the great Jones Falls dam, the Ascutney Mill Dam still survives. It is so highly regarded as a historic monument that in 1970 the American Society of Civil Engineers honoured it as a National Civil Engineering Landmark.

The second highest stone-arch dam built on the Rideau Canal was at Kingston Mills, where the Cataraqui River wound through a low-lying marsh and fell 17 feet over the edge of a granite cliff into a deep rocky gorge, for a total drop of 50 feet. Under the supervision of the masonry contractor, Robert Drummond, canal workers built a massive 30-foot-high stone-arch dam flanked by extensive embankments to prevent the raised waters from flowing around the ends of the dam. This arrangement backed up a navigable depth of water — 20 feet — for 10 miles above the dam to avoid lengthy excavation of the granite river bed at Kingston Mills and flood out the bogs and two rapids upstream. A masonry waste weir, canal basin with a dry-dock extension, four locks (upper detached and three combined), a lockmaster's house, and a blockhouse completed the works. An office was added at the head of the dry dock in 1831, when the Kingston Mills site became the operations headquarters for the Cataraqui section of the canal.

Later hydroelectric developments at Kingston Mills, unlike at Jones Falls, completely transformed the original landscape of the site. The water-power potential of this site had been more or less continually tapped since 1784, when the British government built a grist mill (later adding a sawmill) and dam here to serve the tiny settlement and naval dockyard at Kingston. A succession of private mills replaced the original ones beginning in 1809. In preparation for the building of the canal, the Crown acquired the mill site. It subsequently leased the site to parties interested in developing the hydraulic capacity of the dam.[10] When the Gananoque Light & Water Supply Ltd. (later renamed Gananoque Light & Power Ltd.) leased the mill site from the Crown in 1913, the company immediately demolished an old grist mill on the site and constructed a new dam and waste weir to the rear of the canal structures, replacing the old canal dam and mill pond (plate 1-5). The dam has been

9 Legget, 'The Jones Falls Dam,' pp. 207, 215.
10 Richard Tatley, 'Kingston Mills, A Summary of the Village, its Buildings, Industries and General History, 1783- 1977.' Parks Canada, Manuscript Report No. 413 (1977), p. 7.

backed up with soil and so blends in completely with the landscape. The power company then built a small, plain concrete powerhouse on the west bank of the river and installed a steel-pipe penstock below the waste weir. It provided two dwellings for the powerhouse staff — one was the former miller's house located east of the powerhouse, the second was a new one built near the falls. Both houses still stand and are leased to the present occupants by the company. The two powerhouses at the site today reflect an expansion of the facilities in 1977, when the company installed a second, tiny generator building and new penstock (plate 1-6).

Hydroelectric generation represented a major new development along the Rideau Canal. With the development during the 1870s of reliable electric generators of adequate capacity, it was possible to generate electricity based on the energy contained in flowing water. The product was used initially for electric lighting (the first central electric light stations supplying current to electric arc lamps were not installed in North America until 1879; incandescent lamps were being installed by 1882).[11] By the 1890s electric power was used for a host of applications. At the century's end the importance of hydroelectric generation for the future of Canadian industrial growth was clear, so much so that Thomas C. Keefer devoted his presidential address to the Royal Society of Canada in 1899 to the subject: 'Electrical transmission brings the power to the work,' he said, 'and when the prime mover is water, we have the cheapest power . . . one which is always "on tap" and, like gravity, maintained without cost and applied without delay.'[12]

In Ontario, the availability of cheap water power and the high power demand plus the limitations of the available technology created a network of mostly small, almost entirely hydraulic stations from the late 1890s until the end of World War II.[13] After the war, there occurred a shift to large thermal plants using the heat energy of fossil fuels (coal, oil, or natural gas), or, beginning in the 1960s, uranium. But the advantages of hydroelectric generation, based as it is on a renewable resource and requiring no expensive or unsafe fuels, have led recently to a resurgence of interest in operating small hydroelectric plants.

Gananoque Light & Power Ltd., the company responsible for hydroelectric generation at Jones Falls and Kingston Mills, and also at two other lock stations, (Upper) Brewers and Lower Brewers (renamed Washburn), is one of

11 United States, Department of Commerce and Labour, Bureau of the Census, *Bulletin No. 5, Central Electric Light and Power Stations* (Washington, D.C., 1903), p. 5.

12 Thomas C. Keefer, 'Canadian Water Power and Its Electrical Product in Relation to the Undeveloped Resources of the Dominion,' Royal Society of Canada, *Proceedings and Transactions* 2nd series, 5 (1899): 3.

13 Mark Fram, *Ontario Hydro, Ontario Heritage: A Study of Strategies for the Conservation of the Heritage of Ontario Hydro* (Toronto, 1980), p. 27.

the few privately owned electrical utilities left in the province. This pioneering firm began as a small utility company (Gananoque Electric Light Co.) in 1885 to provide street and factory lighting for the St. Lawrence River town of Gananoque, east of Kingston. A patented Ball Arc Lighting System was employed.[14] The company established a plant on the Gananoque River in 1892 using the building recently vacated by St. Lawrence Steel & Wire at the south end of the Grand Trunk Railway bridge. Two dynamos driven by steam and water power generated direct current for local users.[15]

During 1913 Gananoque Light & Power acquired water rights along the Rideau Canal in the Cataraqui basin for the development of hydro power. One year later, in 1914, it built the first of its Rideau Canal power plants, at Kingston Mills (600 kilowatts).[16] From Kingston Mills, power was sent to Gananoque by a single direct line with no branches. At Gananoque, transformers stepped down the alternating current (long-distance transmission by direct current was impossible) and two 60-kW motor-generator sets converted the current to direct current for distribution locally.[17] Power was also sent to Kingston. In 1917-18 the Gananoque distribution system transferred over to the more efficient alternating current which was and is standard throughout North America. It was because of the increased demand for power in the region after World War I that the company increased the capacity of the Kingston Mills plant, installing a new 1,000-kilovolt-ampere (kVA) unit beside the existing machinery in 1926, and also that of its Gananoque plant.

At the tail end of the Depression, the company embarked on a new expansion program, building a small hydroelectric plant (900 kVA) above Kingston Mills at (Upper) Brewers in 1939 and another (125 kVA) at Washburn in 1942. And once again, it expanded the capacity of its facilities at Gananoque. By World War II Gananoque Light & Power Ltd. had entered into an agreement with another firm to consolidate all hydro power in the area.[18] This resulted in a network of control dams, which were built or acquired on lakes which fed into the south-flowing, Cataraqui River portion of the canal, to establish water-storage areas for the canal and power plants.

During this phase, the descendants of the Tett family of Bedford Mills sold their water rights to Gananoque Light & Power in the 1940s, much to the concern of the citizens of the villages of Newboro and Crosby, to whom the Tetts had been supplying electric power from their tiny Devil Lake installation

14 'Ball Electric Light Co. (Ltd.) of Canada, Toronto,' [trade catalogue] (Toronto, c.1890), pp. 21, 25.

15 The 1892 plant in Gananoque contained a 150-kW d.c. generator, direct-connected to a 200-h.p. horizontal water turbine and a tandem-compound steam engine. The distribution of electricity to the town was by three-wire d.c. at 250 volts. 'Some Historical Notes about Gananoque Light & Power Ltd.' (Typescript supplied by the company and dated November 1982).

16 Ibid. It housed one 900-h.p. horizontal turbine, direct-connected to a 600-kW, 2,400-volt, 3-phase, 60-hz synchronous generator.

17 Ibid. Edison bipolar d.c. generators on either side of a synchronous motor.

18 *Gananoque Reporter*, 18 May 1977.

for several decades.[19] The first dam went in at the head of the 300-foot rocky gorge at Bedford Mills in 1832.[20] The Bedford Mills plant started up around 1897 as an isolated electric plant furnishing light and power for the Tett family's homes and their saw, shingle, and grist mills. It was a crude affair comprising a 6-kW Edison No. 2 bipolar dynamo belt-driven from a counter-shaft in a small powerhouse adjoining the sawmill, with a rope drive from the main shaft of the mill's waterwheel (probably a turbine) to the countershaft.[21] The family enlarged the capacity to 37½ kW in 1916, when it extended the power line from Newboro to Crosby. Although the Bedford Mills plant eventually closed in 1949, it is still possible today to see the dam (rebuilt), ruins of the old penstock and concrete silo (where locals say the turbine was located), and remains of a sawmill-turned-generating-station for producing and transmitting electric light and power on a limited basis.

Following the war the local demand for power increased to such an extent that Gananoque Light & Power constructed the powerhouse and a single wood-stave penstock at Jones Falls, its largest plant on the Rideau Canal. When it installed the final generating unit and two additional penstocks in 1956, the capacity of the Jones Falls plant was raised to 3,225 kVA; later additions have roughly doubled its total capacity. In 1972 it was automated with radio remote control from Gananoque. In keeping with the new general trend away from operating small hydroelectric plants, the company constructed a 2,500-kVA thermal generating station just north of Gananoque in 1959-60. Capacity was enlarged in 1968 and 1982 to make it one of the largest plants of this type in Ontario. It produces power with dual-fuel (natural gas and diesel fuel) reciprocating engines. In 1972 the company replaced the existing transmission interconnection with Kingston with an interconnection to Ontario Hydro grid at Gananoque. Also, it abandoned the small Washburn plant.

By the late 1970s small hydroelectric facilities were once again in vogue, and in 1977 the Kingston Mills plant received a third unit (500 kVA). The Washburn plant was completely rehabilitated and restored to service with its capacity increased in 1984. The company has remained in family hands, and today is presided over by the grandson of the original owners. In addition to delivering electricity to close to three thousand customers in Gananoque and the rural area west from there to the city limits of Kingston, the company is looking into proposals to rehabilitate other small hydroelectric plants on the Rideau Canal.

19 Queen's University Archives, Tett Papers, Transfer Case 4, Folder 4, item 27, 'Electrical Installation, J.P. Tett & Bro., 1917;' Transfer Case 9, Folder 29, 'To Operate an Alternating Current Transmission Line. J.P. Tett, 1925,' and Folder 30, item 361, 'Agreement re: Electric Power for Newboro, 1938.' See also *Westport Mirror* 7 December 1916 ('by-law granting to J.P. Tett & Bro. the right to supply electric light, heat, and power within the township of North Crosby') and 13 November 1944.

20 Osborne and Swainson, *Dividing the Waters*, p. 37.

21 Queen's University Archives, Tett Papers, Transfer Case 15, Folder 7, various notes on the original electric plant at Bedford Mills, dated c.1897.

Another of the important changes in technology along the Rideau Canal has been the development of new methods of transportation. At present on the canal (including the 6-mile Tay Branch Canal to the town of Perth) there are a total of 42 bridge crossings, six of which are railway bridges.[22] It is commonly assumed that the coming of the railway destroyed the commercial potential of the Rideau Canal, but that was decidedly not the case. The cost of handling and freighting the mainly bulky, low-value commodities of the region usually proved too great for rail transport. It was more a case of railway service complementing commercial navigation on the Rideau. In any event, government authorities have always insisted that the water-borne traffic has priority over land transport, and this policy affected engineering choices when it came to designing and constructing railway (and road) bridges over the canal.

The first railway bridge to cross the Rideau Canal was constructed at Kingston Mills by the Grand Trunk Railway c.1855 as part of its main line connecting Montreal and Toronto. A railway crossing here for an east-west line was natural, as this was the narrowest section of the Cataraqui River. The Grand Trunk's crossing comprised a single-track, high-level fixed bridge of three spans, one of which crossed over the upper lock of the flight of locks, the others crossed over the course of the Cataraqui River to the east of the locks (plate 1-7).[23] The superstructure was comprised of wrought-iron tubular or box girders some 310 feet overall with the rails running above. Dressed stone piers and abutments provided a generous 22-foot 8-inch clearance over the water level of the canal lock below. The Grand Trunk completely rebuilt the bridge in 1890 to accommodate the double-tracking of its main line.[24] While it maintained the existing alignment of the bridge at Kingston Mills, it had to enlarge the original piers and abutments, rebuilding them to the same height as the original and in dressed stone as before. A through Warren steel truss crossed the canal lock and two deck trusses spanned the river portion. The railway bridge one sees at Kingston Mills today was built in 1929, when the successor to the Grand Trunk, Canadian National Railways, replaced the truss spans with a modern through plate-girder span over the canal lock and deck plate girders over the two river spans (plate 1-8).[25] A reinforced concrete river pier replaced the former one of dressed stone, and the east and west abutments of 1890 have undergone substantial concrete repair work.

A second major but far different rail crossing can be found at Smiths Falls,

22 Robert Passfield, 'Swing Bridges on the Rideau Canal,' *IA: Journal of the Society for Industrial Archeology* 2, 1 (1976): 59. The bridges are listed in Legget, *Rideau Waterway*, pp. 290-92.
23 Referred to by the G.T.R. as the 'Rideau'. Parks Canada, 'Rideau Canal. Preliminary Site Study Series No. 3, Kingston Mills Lock' (Ottawa, 1975), p. 81; and Tatley, 'Kingston Mills,' p. 74.
24 Parks Canada, 'Kingston Mills Lock,' p. 82.
25 Parks Canada, 'Kingston Mills Lock,' p. 55.

where a single-leaf bascule bridge — a Scherzer Rolling Lift-type — carried the Ottawa-Toronto branch of the Canadian Northern Railway across the canal. It is the only bascule railway bridge to be built over the Rideau Canal; the others, like the one at Kingston Mills, are fixed high-level spans. Without the construction of long approaches, the bridging of rivers and canals whose banks are very low require a movable span or spans. Until the late nineteenth century the most practical, hence common, type of movable bridge for carrying road or railway traffic across navigable waterways was the swing bridge. The balanced swing span was pivoted on a pier mid-stream in the navigation channel. But there were serious drawbacks: the pier subdivided the navigation channel, and both the centre pier and open span presented a hazard to shipping. Long-span bascule bridges were impractical because they required the development of both a practical method of counterbalancing the open span and a suitable power system for their operation. Only with the innovation of electric power and individual electric motors in the late nineteenth century could a practical new bascule form be developed.[26]

The Scherzer Rolling Lift bridge was the invention of William Scherzer, who patented the bridge type in 1893 and founded a company in Chicago to manufacture it.[27] The novelty and advantage of Scherzer's design was that the arm, supported on a pair of large rockers, rolled away from the navigable channel on a perfectly smooth and level track. To provide horizontal stability, lugs on the track engaged in slots on the underside of the rockers. The rolling motion all but eliminated the type of friction involved with the traditional trunion bascule, where the entire weight of the movable arm revolved about a hinged pivot. Also, with the Scherzer the arm moves backward as it moves upward, thus it provides a maximum channel width for navigation with minimum span length (plate 1-10). Unlike swing bridges, Scherzer bridges could be built side by side to provide multi-track crossings for railroads.

The company designed and built its bridges in many styles throughout the world. It also contracted work granting the right, for a fee, to construct them. The Scherzer bridge constructed at Smiths Falls in 1911-13 is the work of the Dominion Bridge Company of Lachine, Quebec. This was not the first of the Scherzer Rolling Lift type to be built in Canada, but it is the oldest of the 14 that survive in this country. The first one built in Canada was opened in 1911, a 50-foot span over a side harbour basin of the Lachine Canal at Côte St. Paul.[28]

26 The large vertical lift bridge was an innovation at the end of the nineteenth century. The first in North America was J.A.L. Waddell's Halstead Street Bridge, Chicago, constructed in 1894. It had a 130-foot span and afforded 155 feet of vertical clearance.

27 The Scherzer Company issued catalogues in 1897, 1901, and 1908. The 1901 edition has been consulted here. The firm of Hazelet & Erdal, Consulting Engineers, succeeded the company in 1936.

28 This information and the technical description which follows relies heavily on Robert Passfield's 23-page unpublished report, 'The C.N.R. Scherzer Rolling Lift Bascule Bridge, Smiths Falls, Ontario' (Staff Report, Historic Sites and Monuments Board of Canada, Parks Canada, June 1983).

Dozens of improved bascule bridges were built in Canada after 1911, but very few were of the Scherzer type. (The highway lift bridge, built in 1917, carrying the Lasalle Causeway across the entrance to the Rideau Waterway at Kingston is an example of the more common type, a Strauss heel trunion bascule.)

At Smiths Falls, the Scherzer Rolling Lift crosses the canal cut 350 feet above the upper detached lock. There are two deck plate girder approach spans (67 feet 4 inches and 37 feet 4 inches in length) set on concrete piers and abutments. These raise the bridge 8½ feet above the level of water to allow small boats to pass under it without having to open the bridge. The lifting portion consists of a plate girder 69 feet in length. At the business end of the movable arm are the massive segmental rockers constructed of steel plate reinforced with ribs. Poised at the end of the rockers is a large reinforced concrete counterweight balancing the weight of the arm stretching across the water (plate I-11). The movable arm was operated from the catwalk outside the bridge-tender's cabin, mounted on a high wooden framework to the east side of the approach span, at the heel of the lift.

This particular bridge was originally designed to be operated either manually or by an electric motor. When the small direct-current motor was installed in 1914, it took only one minute for the operator to roll back or lower the arm by 90 degrees. But a year later the town replaced direct current with alternating current, rendering the motor useless. The railway decided to operate the bridge by hand, and continued to do so until it ended service on the line in December 1978. Although operating the bridge by hand took much longer — 10 to 15 minutes to raise it by 45 to 60 degrees, or 20 minutes to raise it the full 90 degrees — than with the motor, with no canal traffic in winter and only light rail traffic during the canal season, it was possible simply to leave the arm in one position most of the time.

In 1982 Canadian National Railways applied to the Canadian Transport Commission for permission to abandon the Smiths Falls station. Although the railway also intended to apply for permission to remove the tracks, including the lift bridge, it was willing to offer the railway facilities to interested parties. Accordingly, a local group quickly formed a Smiths Falls Railway and Museum Association and made plans to save the bridge and railway station located about a mile east of the crossing. As a first step, the association succeeded in having the bridge and station declared a National Historic Site in 1984. In spite of the good intentions of Parks Canada, however, the bridge sits rusting away away in the permanent upright position; few who see it know or care about its history or significance (plate 1-12).

By the time Parks Canada took over responsibility for the canal in 1972, the old managers, the Department of Transport, had already electrified and added steel gates to the locks at Newboro and Black Rapids, and begun construction of a massive new, reinforced-concrete, electrically operated lock to replace three standard combined locks at Smiths Falls. The new single lock, opened in 1973, provides a drop of 26 feet to the main river channel and incorporates a modern concrete road bridge at Beckwith Street (Highway 15) designed to provide ample clearance beneath it for vessels using the new high lock (plate 1-14). (The concrete bridge replaced the old swing bridge across the old combined locks. The new bridge was fought for by local townspeople, who argued the need to eliminate the bottleneck created each summer by the canal traffic through this popular stretch of the Rideau.) The three combined locks it replaced remain intact and empty as canal artifacts for tourists to visit. The old locks, however, are neglected and in very poor condition.

The electrically operated lock at Smiths Falls is efficient to operate. It fills in 7 to 20 minutes and empties even faster, depending in both cases on the number and size of the craft locking through. From the control panel located at the upper end, canal operators communicate with water traffic below using closed-circuit television and telephones. But breakdowns in the electrically operated oil hydraulic system are frequent and repairs complex, hence costly. The electrical switches which operate the pump for the hydraulic system, for example, often short out. A power failure in the town of Smiths Falls will paralyze the lock. Leaks and breaks in the oil line require outside experts for repairs. All this can lead to delays for the recreational craft on the canal, where a total of approximately 100,000 lockages were recorded for the 24 lock stations in 1987.

Parks Canada has halted the trend toward electrification of the Rideau Canal, and today the locks at most of the stations retain their hand-operated machinery, and massive wooden gates still pivot on iron-clad heel posts (plate 1-13). Yet government officials appear to have no clear or consistent policy when it comes to recognizing the historic value of the new twentieth-century technology along the system. At Jones Falls, for example, visitors to the famous horseshoe dam of 1832 are able to stand on a platform built above the penstocks of the Gananoque Light & Power hydroelectric installation for a side view of the stone face of the dam. There they can read all about the history of the dam but absolutely nothing about the power plant below them, even though the plant is an integral part of the evolving history of the dam site and, indeed, of the entire Heritage Canal.

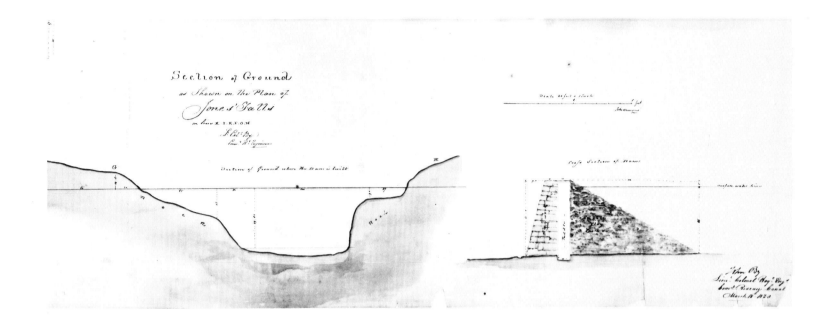

I-I   Section of plan of Jones Falls signed by Lt. Col. John By, 18 March 1830. Right: 'Cross Section of Dam;' left: 'Section of Ground where the Dam is built.' *National Archives of Canada* (c-12892)

1-2   'The Great Dam at Jones' Falls; from the West end,' by Thomas Burrowes, 1841. *Archives of Ontario*

1-3
Jones Falls dam, 1980.

1-4
Penstocks and generating station, Jones
Falls, 1980.

I-5   The falls and abandoned mill, Kingston Mills, by John Boyd, 20 May 1913. *National Archives of Canada* (PA-61026)

1-6
Penstocks and generating station, Kingston
Mills, 1987.

I-7   Grand Trunk Railway bridge under construction, Kingston Mills, by Thomas Burrowes, c. 1855. *Archives of Ontario*

1-8
Canadian National Railways bridge,
Kingston Mills, 1987.

1-9
Former Canadian Northern Railway Scherzer
bridge, Smiths Falls, 1978.

I-IO   'The 275-Foot Span Double Track Scherzer Rolling Lift Bridge . . . across the south branch of the Chicago River . . . also shows channel obstructed by 12th Street Swing Bridge,' from the catalogue of the Scherzer Rolling Lift Bridge Company, Chicago, 1901. *National Gallery of Canada, Ottawa*

I-II
Detail, Scherzer Bridge, Smiths Falls, 1978.

1-12
Disused Scherzer bridge, Smiths
Falls, 1987.

1-13
Hand-operated locks, Jones Falls,
1980.

1-14   New lock and highway bridge, Smiths Falls, 1987.

The Grand Trunk Railway has always had a bad press in Canada. The original agreement between Francis Hincks, Inspector General of the Province of Canada, and the consortium of British contractors, Peto, Brassey, Betts & Jackson, for the construction of the Montreal-Toronto section, whereby the contractors would help in the raising of British capital for the railway yet to be organized, aroused the ire of all those who claimed that the railway could be built by Canadians and largely financed in Canada. The Grand Trunk, incorporated in 1852, became pictured in this country as the 'corporate offspring of English contractors, promoters and financiers'.[1] Its critics accused its management of incompetence, extravagance and corruption — charges that have sullied the reputation of the railway to the present day. Yet, although almost every aspect of the Grand Trunk was the object of criticism, its bridges and stations, apart from the locations of the latter, were almost free from censure.

The Grand Trunk was to be the longest railway in the world at the time — more than 1,000 miles — with its main line running from Portland, Maine, on the Atlantic, via Montreal and Toronto, to Point Edward, just north of Sarnia, at the outlet of Lake Huron. At Point Edward, it would connect with American lines via a car ferry across the St. Clair River. The inevitable profitability of the project as painted in the prospectus of 1853[2] soon proved to be a piece of puffery, and the railway was in financial straits for much of its history. Nevertheless the Grand Trunk continually expanded its operations and by 1880 had its own direct connection with Chicago. The American, Charles M. Hays, who became general manager of the G.T.R. in 1896, is generally credited with a masterly reorganization of the railway, but it was Hays who led it into the 'colossal blunder of invading the Canadian West'[3] with construction of the Grand Trunk Pacific between 1907 and 1914.

When the Canadian government formed the Canadian National Railways to salvage the mess resulting from the overbuilding of railways in Canada in the early years of this century, the new system needed an efficient, busy, working road to provide it with any hope of viability. The G.T.R., which could no longer meet its financial obligations to the Grand Trunk Pacific, but which had a large through traffic between Chicago and the Atlantic seaboard, was taken over and in 1923 became part of the newly incorporated Canadian National Railway Company.

2

Early Grand Trunk Railway Bridges and Stations

1 H.A. Lovett, *Canada and the Grand Trunk 1829-1924* (n.p., n.d.), p. 51.

2 *Statements, Reports and Accounts of the Grand Trunk Railway Company of Canada* (Toronto, 1857), pp. 5-14.

3 Lovett, *Canada and the Grand Trunk*, p. 233.

The strongest opposition to Hincks's plan to build the railway with British capital and contractors came from A.T. Galt and his associates L.H. Holton and D.L. Macpherson. Galt was president, with C.S. Gzowski chief engineer, of the St. Lawrence & Atlantic Railway, which with its American counterpart, the Atlantic & St. Lawrence, had been built between Montreal and Portland, Maine. Galt and his associates also controlled both the Montreal & Kingston, which held a charter to build between those two cities, and the Toronto & Guelph Railway, on which construction had begun. When all three Canadian railways were incorporated into the Grand Trunk in 1853, the railway awarded the contract for the construction of the 172 miles between Toronto and Sarnia to the contracting firm of Galt and his group, C.S. Gzowski & Company. The Canadian contractors were to be paid in cash as the work progressed; the British contractors were to receive debentures and shares in the railway. Galt and his associates made fortunes from their adroit dealings; the English contractors estimated that they lost £1,000,000 on their contract.

The contracts called for 'the construction of a first-class single-track railway, with the foundations of all the large structures sufficient for a double line, equal in permanence and stability to any railway in England'.[4] Critics scoffed at the line between Montreal and Toronto supposedly being equal to a first-class English railway. It was said, with some justification, to be poorly located, laid with bad rails that broke, and inadequately ballasted. The line west of Toronto was highly praised, on the other hand. Much credit was given to Gzowski & Co., though most, if not all, of the work was done by subcontractors (as happened with the Montreal-Toronto section). It was Walter Shanly, the divisional chief engineer, and his brother Francis Shanly, the resident engineer, who were really responsible for the excellent construction of the Toronto and Sarnia division.

To provide a connection across the St. Lawrence River at Montreal between the former St. Lawrence & Atlantic Railway and the Montreal-Toronto line, the Grand Trunk's first chief engineer, Alexander McKenzie Ross, drew plans for an iron tubular bridge. Ross had been one of the resident engineers under Robert Stephenson on the Chester & Holyhead Railway in Britain, and had been in charge of the masonry of the Conway Tubular Bridge,[5] which had served as a prototype for Stephenson's famous Britannia Bridge spanning the Menai Strait between Wales and Anglesey. The superstructure of both bridges

4 *Statements, Reports and Accounts of the Grand Trunk Railway Company*, p. 12.
5 J.C. Jeaffreson, *The Life of Robert Stephenson . . .* , second edition (London, 1866), Vol. II, p. 199.

consisted of massive iron girders, made up of riveted wrought-iron plates with vertical stiffening ribs, and was of hollow rectangular section large enough for a train to travel through. Ross consulted Stephenson, who was appointed engineer-in-chief of the proposed bridge named after the Queen. In the summer of 1853 Stephenson visited Canada to personally examine the site. Construction began in 1854. A mile and a quarter in length (its abutments and embankments extended for a total of about another half mile into the river), the Victoria Bridge was to be the largest in the world at the time. It was also the last of the great tubular bridges and the last major work with which Stephenson was associated. The famous engineer died on October 12, 1859, exactly two months before the first freight train to Portland crossed the bridge. It was not until 1897-98 that the iron superstructure was dismantled and replaced by a steel lattice truss.

The contract with Peto, Brassey, Betts & Jackson specified that 'all Viaducts or large structures' were to be 'composed of masonry piers and abutments, and either arched of similar material or covered with wrought iron beams.'[6] In fact no masonry arch viaducts were built, and all 'large structures', whether constructed by the British contractors or Gzowski & Co., had iron plate-girder superstructures. (The bridge at Napanee has four stone arches at each end.) Individual spans of more than about 70 feet in length, such as the crossing at Kingston Mills, seen under construction in plate 1-7, were modelled after the box beam or tubular girder (but with the track on top) developed for the Britannia and Conway bridges by Robert Stephenson in association with William Fairbairn and Professor Eaton Hodgkinson.

C.H. Gregory,[7] the distinguished English engineer whom the London board of the Grand Trunk sent out in 1857 to report on the work of the contractors, confirmed that part of the line between Kingston and Toronto had been poorly ballasted, but he essentially defended the work done under the contract of Peto, Brassey, Betts & Jackson. He was particularly impressed with the construction in about five months of the 23 miles from Grafton to Newtonville, 'although it comprised the Port Hope Viaduct, and about twelve miles of heavy work — an example of energy rarely surpassed.'[8] The viaduct spanning the narrow valley of the Ganaraska River almost at the harbour of Port Hope had 55 spans varying from $25\frac{1}{2}$ feet to 60 feet across the river itself (plate 2-2). The piers were built of brick on high stone foundations intended

6 'General Specification for Works of Construction,' *Journals of the Legislative Assembly of the Province of Canada,* Appendix No. 13, 1856.

7 (Sir) Charles Hutton Gregory is best known for his introduction of the railway semaphore signal in 1841.

8 *Proceedings of the Fourth Annual General Meeting of the Shareholders of the Grand Trunk Railway Company of Canada . . . 29th September, 1857* (Montreal, 1857), p. 30.

to provide protection against the river's severe spring floods. The viaduct, just over 1,800 feet long, was completely rebuilt with stone piers and the number of spans reduced to 31 in 1893, during the double-tracking of the Montreal-Toronto section. The G.T.R. constructed the present steel superstructure about 1910 (plate 2-3). Embankments and concrete arch abutments built at each end of the bridge have since reduced the number of spans to 20.

Work on the Port Hope Viaduct was completed shortly before the railway opened the line between Montreal and Toronto on October 27, 1856. 'There was nothing very peculiar about its opening,' the Port Hope *Guide* reported. 'Quite a number of citizens went to the DEPOT through the wet, to see the first regular passenger train from Toronto. No cannons were fired, no address read, nor any palates moistened with champagne in honour of the occasion. — Little time would there have been for any demonstration, as the train [of three first-class and three second-class cars] only remained about ten minutes.'[9] Champagne had 'trickled delightfully down the throats of the thirsty' at two celebrations held by the local subcontractors the previous month, when 'several hundred people availed themselves of the opportunity to test the merit of the far famed and much abused Grand Trunk Railway.'[10]

On the Toronto & Guelph Railway some bridge construction had begun before the railway was amalgamated with the Grand Trunk. On April 4, 1853, Walter Shanly instructed his brother Francis, the resident engineer, that 'the character of many of the structures' was to be changed now that the railway was to form part of the Grand Trunk line to Sarnia, and 'all trestle work . . . [was] to be done away with'.[11] He issued orders also to abandon work on the foundations for the wooden truss viaduct planned for the major crossing of the Credit Valley just east of Georgetown. The redesigned bridge, completed in 1855, had seven piers rising to a height of 115 feet above the river. The piers and abutments of local sandstone supported iron tubular girders, 7 feet square, forming eight spans of 96 feet each, with the track on top (plate 2-4). C.W. Young wrote in his 'Reminiscences of Georgetown' that when he was a schoolboy, 'it was considered a daredevil trick to walk through the tube, and if a train happened to go over it while we were inside it was a matter to be bragged about, even if we were half deaf with the racket.'[12]

The Credit Valley Viaduct was the largest of the bridges spanning the rivers and valleys west of Toronto. In his report of 1857, Gregory wrote that he had

9 Port Hope *Guide*, 1 November 1856.
10 Ibid., 11 September 1856.
11 Frank Norman Walker, ed., *Daylight through the Mountain: Letters and Labours of Civil Engineers Walter and Francis Shanly* (Montreal, 1957), p. 263.
12 C.W. Young, 'Reminiscences of Georgetown,' Georgetown Women's Institute Tweedsmuir History, Halton Hills Public Library (Georgetown).

'rarely seen a work of finer design or execution'.[13] After the Grand Trunk amalgamated with the Great Western in 1882, the former Great Western trackage to the south via London became the main line to Sarnia and the American West. As a result, the Credit Valley Viaduct has remained a single-track bridge to the present day. Nevertheless the increasing weight of trains at the turn of the century made it necessary to replace the iron tubular girders. Before the erection of the existing steel superstructure in 1906, the east abutment was rebuilt in concrete and the rest of the original substructure more or less completely renewed (plate 2-5).

The G.T.R. constructed two impressive bridges at St. Marys in the 1850s — the Thames River Bridge on the main line to Sarnia, and Trout Creek Bridge on the branch line to London — 'the two together forming,' in the words of a contemporary writer, 'the greatest ornament in engineering to any town in Canada West.'[14] Today the Thames River Bridge, completed in 1859, is only used by an occasional freight, as the railway has abandoned the old main line west of Parkhill. The slightly higher and longer Trout Creek Bridge, on the other hand, is still very much in use, with four passenger trains a day each way between Toronto and London via St. Marys (plate 2-7). Except for the replacement of the original iron plate girders with a steel superstructure in 1912 (plate 2-6), this bridge has been little changed since it was built in 1857-58. It has 12 spans of 66½ feet carrying the single track nearly 70 feet above the creek bed. The piers and abutments of the excellent local limestone were built by local subcontractors. It is not clear from an advertisement of Alex McDonald & Co. in the *St. Mary's Weekly Argus*, 20 August 1857, for 'about twenty Masons and 100 Laborers, also a number of Quarrymen wanted to work upon the Grand Trunk Viaduct', to which of the two bridges this advertisement refers. A similar advertisement appeared the following week when the other local contractors, Cameron & Noakes, sought 'Twenty Double Teams' in addition to masons, quarrymen and labourers.[15]

Frederick Cumberland, chief engineer of the Ontario, Simcoe & Huron Railway, wrote of the Grand Trunk's masonry and iron girder bridges that 'whilst their simplicity satisfies the feeling of the most prudent economy, their materials are so exceptional, the character of the workmanship so excellent, and the taste of their finish so fitting, that one is satisfied with them as works of the most substantial permanence.'[16] The masonry piers and abutments of

13 *Proceedings of the Fourth Annual Meeting of the . . . Grand Trunk Railway*, p. 34.
14 *The Semi-Weekly Spectator*, Hamilton, 23 November 1859.
15 *St. Mary's Weekly Argus*, 27 August 1857.
16 Frederick Cumberland, 'Some Notes of a Visit to the Works of the Grand Trunk Railway, west of Toronto, February, 1855,' *The Canadian Journal* 3 (May 1855): 227.

many of the Grand Trunk's bridges of the 1850s, including the Victoria Bridge at Montreal, still survive, as do many of the railway's early stations.

The Toronto *Colonist's* scathing reference to the 'miserable shanties, called Station Houses'[17] was most unusual even for the harshest critics of the Grand Trunk. It was generally acknowledged that the railway's buildings 'of the most solid and substantial masonry . . . in no way belie[d] the promises of the company as to the character of the works along the line.'[18] The 'General Specification for Works of Construction' had called for the station buildings 'to be of stone or brick, and covered with tin or slate at the option of the Contractors.'[19] When Ross, the chief engineer, found that there was a demand for more stations than had been originally planned, he proposed to cover the cost of additional stations by adopting more economical wooden construction. However, as Ross himself wrote, 'the idea of substituting timber for brick and stone, created at the time so loud a clamour throughout the country generally, participated in by the representatives in Parliament, that the demand for brick and stone had to a great extent to be submitted to.'[20]

Seven of the nine surviving early Grand Trunk stations in Ontario — at Prescott, Ernestown, Napanee, Brighton, Port Hope, Georgetown, and St. Marys — are single-storey structures built to a standard design illustrated by the drawing of a 'Second Class Way Side Station', plate 2-8. The smallest of these stations, at Ernestown, Napanee and Brighton, have only five bays, while the largest, at Prescott, has seven. The details of the masonry also vary from station to station. Two somewhat similar stations but with one and a half storeys survive at Belleville and Kingston, the latter now converted into a restaurant. An early photograph of the station at Belleville, plate 2-9, confirms it too was originally a one-storey building of the standard design. Brighton is the sole remaining station to be built of brick rather than stone, and it is only at St. Marys that the uniform bays with double doors and a transom above were retained over the years (plate 2-12). At the other stations, most of the doorways were filled in to sill height and changed into windows; evidence of this is often visible in the masonry. With the exception of the stations at Ernestown and St. Marys, a projecting bay to give the telegrapher a clear view of the line was added in later years to the single-storey stations, thereby spoiling the classical simplicity of their original facades.

17 Quoted in Montreal *Transcript,* 9 September 1857.
18 *Brockville Recorder,* 12 July 1855.
19 *Journals of the Legislative Assembly,* Appendix No. 13, 1856.
20 *Statements, Reports and Accounts of the Grand Trunk Railway,* p. 42.

The design of these stations has been attributed to Francis Thompson, the English railway architect who worked for the G.T.R. during its construction. Thompson, who was born in 1808, first came to Canada as a young man in 1830 and worked as an architect in Montreal, where he designed St. Paul's Anglican Church. He returned to England after the death of his first wife in 1838, and, like Alexander McKenzie Ross, became associated with Robert Stephenson, for whom he did the architectural design of the Conway and Britannia bridges. In 1853 Thompson came back to Canada to be architect for the G.T.R., until finally returning to England in 1859.[21] Thompson is known to have been the architect of the Victoria Bridge, the Grand Trunk's large Portland station built 1855-56 and demolished in 1902, and the extensive engine house and repair shops at Island Pond, Vermont, built 1857-58, but there is yet no evidence that he designed the early Canadian stations.

Their simple Italianate design is not unlike that of certain early English stations, but those stations were not designed by Francis Thompson. The attribution to him of the design for the Canadian stations is made somewhat more problematic by the fact that another architect, Thomas Seaton Scott, was working as architect for the Grand Trunk's British contractors. Scott, who was later the first chief architect of the Department of Public Works of Canada, was born in England in 1826. He came to Canada, according to his obituary in the Ottawa *Journal*, 'during the building of the Victoria Bridge, and was employed on that work up to its completion.'[22] He continued his connection with the Grand Trunk during the rest of his career, and designed the second Union Station, Toronto (1871-73), and Bonaventure Station, Montreal (1889), both of which have long since been demolished. Though Scott's responsibilities in the 1850s were probably the appointment of subcontractors and supervision of their work on the site, the attribution of the early station design to Francis Thompson remains uncertain.

The exterior design of the stations with their uniform bays gives no hint of their interior layout, but fortunately a surviving drawing for the station at Georgetown includes a plan (plate 2-10), besides elevations similar to those of the 'Second Class Way Side Station'. Four box stoves, one of which was located between the telegraph office and the ticket office, heated the building. The heating must have been made more difficult by the doors in the end walls, and it is hard to conjecture what practical purpose those doors served.

21 Biographical information on Francis Thompson was generously given by Robert G. Hill, editor and compiler of the forthcoming *Biographical Dictionary of Architects in Canada 1800-1950*.
22 Ottawa *Journal*, 17 June 1895.

Georgetown is the most altered of the surviving stations with its raised roof, tower, dormers, and projecting bays (plate 2-14). The date of the alterations has been said to be 1904, but in 1892, a year after the former Northern & Northwestern track had been realigned so that it crossed the Grand Trunk tracks at the station, the *Acton Free Press* reported that the station 'has been enlarged and repaired recently and is now the best station between Guelph and Toronto.'[23]

The Grand Trunk's decision to locate most stations on the outskirts of the town or village was the subject of much criticism. The railway defended the decision on the grounds that land was cheaper there, and it did not have to acquire expensive rights-of-way. There was considerable land speculation and subdividing of lots, however, near the stations, which were often located on land owned by politically influential people. This is illustrated at St. Marys, where the remote site belonged to the mayor of London, and the reeve of the village, the village clerk, and a councillor owned neighbouring properties. A letter to the local newspaper in December 1858 opposed the building of a gravel road to the station, which the local firm of McDonald & Anderson had constructed that year. 'Why, Sir,' wrote the indignant citizen, 'the Station will stand a monument of the stupidity of some and the cupidity of others of our Council for ages. Generations yet unborn will point to it as indicative of the mental calibre of the public men of our village in the year of Grace, 1858.'[24] It was not until 1879 that the railway built a station in the town, approximately two blocks south of the present station built in 1907 at the south end of Trout Creek Bridge. Today the old stone station of 1858, now known as St. Marys Junction, is a National Historic Site, yet it stands abandoned, boarded up, fenced around, and deteriorating.

There was little or no concern at the demolition of some of the Grand Trunk's early stations, such as that at Shannonville in 1972. The Grand Trunk had never captured the imagination of the public like the Canadian Pacific, which many people today mistakenly think of as Canada's first railway, and these stations were in small communities, so that their loss was virtually unnoticed. Though the problem of station preservation is a complex one, and the case of St. Marys Junction is not encouraging, there has been considerable progress recently. When Canadian National Railways announced in 1979 that the Port Hope station, which was in poor condition, was to be torn down and

23 *Acton Free Press*, 27 October 1892.
24 *St. Mary's Weekly Argus*, 2 December 1858.

53

replaced by a modern metal and glass shelter, there was a local outcry. The railway was persuaded to revoke its decision to demolish the station and, in collaboration with VIA Rail (a separate corporation for passenger service), join with the Architectural Conservancy of Ontario, the Ontario Heritage Foundation, and the Ontario Ministry of Citizenship & Culture in a major restoration project. The soft local limestone had weathered badly, and both end walls had to be completely rebuilt with sandstone from southern Quebec since suitable limestone was unobtainable. The organizations involved completed the project in 1985 (plate 2-13). Work has recently begun on some restoration of Georgetown station, and a restoration is planned of Napanee station.

GRAND TRUNK RAILWAY.

Contract No. ___23___ Kingston.

SCHEDULE OF PRICES FOR MASONRY, &C.,
IN ANNEXED CONTRACT MENTIONED.

	£	s.	D.
TOOLED ASHLAR—in Parapets, Coping, String Course, and Arch, at per Cubic Foot,	—	3	6
FINE BOUCHARDING—in do. do. do. do., at per Cubic Foot,	—	3	4
TOOLED ASHLAR—in Piers, Abutments, Wing Walls, including backing. at per Cubic Foot,	—	1	6
FINE BOUCHARDING—in do. do. do. do., at per Cubic Foot,	—	1	4
COURSE BOUCHARDING—in do. do. do. do., at per Cubic Foot,	—	1	2
ROCK FACED WORK—in do. do. do. do., at per Cubic Foot,	—	1	—
COURSED RUBBLE—in do. do. do. do., at per Cubic Foot	—	—	7½

2 per foot Extra if set in cement

D l Roblin

2-1
'Schedule of prices for masonry, &c.,' for a contract between Peto, Brassey, Betts & Jackson and David Roblin of Napanee, c. 1854. *Lennox & Addington County Museum*

2-2   Port Hope Viaduct, c. 1856. *National Archives of Canada* (PA-127489)

2-3   Train 68 from Toronto to Montreal crossing the Port Hope Viaduct, 1987.

2-4   Credit Valley Viaduct, by William Armstrong, 1855. *Royal Ontario Museum, Toronto*

2-5   Credit Valley Viaduct, 1988.

2-6   Replacing the girders, Trout Creek Bridge, St. Marys, by R.W. Gray, 1912. *L.W. Pfaff*

2-7   Train 85 from Toronto to Sarnia crossing Trout Creek Bridge, St. Marys, 1987.

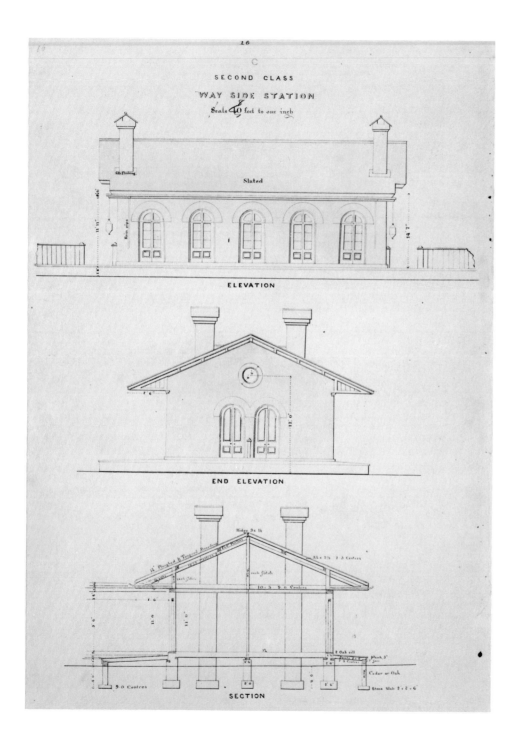

2-8
'Second Class Way Side Station.' *Shanly Papers, Archives of Ontario*

2-9
G.T.R. station, Belleville, c. 1860. *Hastings County Museum*

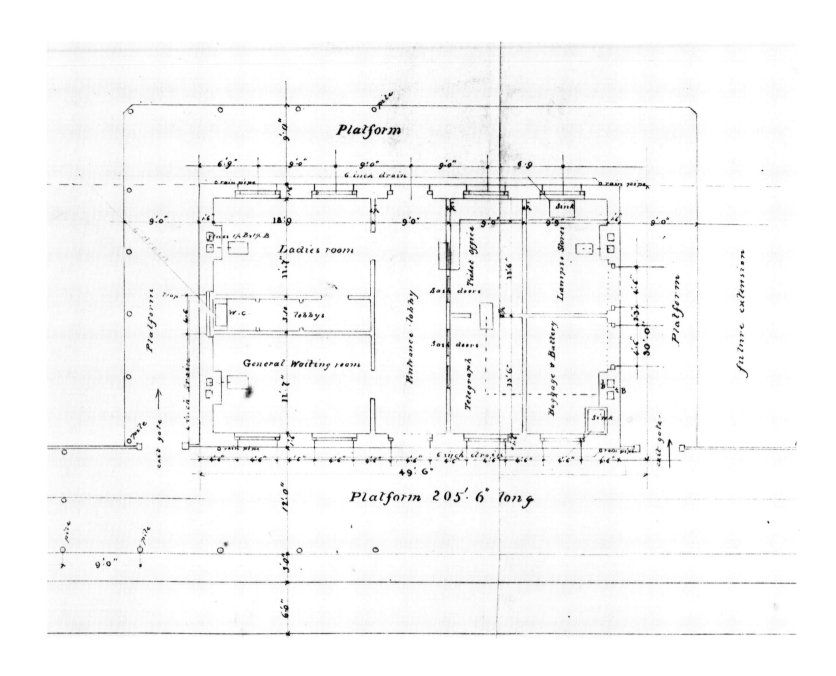

2-10　Plan of G.T.R. station, Georgetown, c. 1855. *National Archives of Canada* (c-97798)

2-11   Shannonville station, 1971.

2-12 St. Marys Junction, 1979.

2-13   Port Hope station, 1987.

2-14   Georgetown station, 1987. (The outline in the end wall shows where there was once an adjoining freight shed.)

3

The Hamilton Pumphouse

Epidemics of cholera and typhoid and devastating fires led to a demand for public water-supply systems in the growing cities of mid-nineteenth-century North America. The increasing use of water for industrial purposes contributed to the pollution created by cesspools and the absence of sewers, and at the same time added to the need for an ample as well as clean water supply. The design of complex urban waterworks systems, the majority of which depended upon pumping to elevated reservoirs for distribution by gravity flow, now became a major branch of engineering.

In September 1854, after a summer in which Hamilton had suffered severely from the worst outbreak of cholera to hit the Province of Canada, the city's Committee on Fire and Water announced the holding of a competition for 'Plans, Specifications and Estimates, for supplying 40,000 inhabitants with water from Burlington Bay . . . accompanied with Specifications and estimates for Engine House, Engine, Pumps, Reservoirs, Pipes, etc.'[1] In 1850 the city had a population of only 11,000, but it was now growing rapidly, since it had become the headquarters for the Great Western Railway, the first trunk line in Canada. (In 1853 the *American Railroad Journal* reported that the railway's depot and shops were being built 'of a size calculated to astonish even those who had made the largest calculations as to Western progress.' Its car shops were 'not only the largest workshop of the kind, but perhaps, the most extensive manufacturing establishment of any description in Western Canada.')[2]

The competition was judged by Thomas Coltrin Keefer, then chief engineer of the Montreal Water Works. Keefer was born in Thorold, Upper Canada, in 1821. After attending Upper Canada College in Toronto, he worked for two years on the Erie Canal, but returned to Canada in 1840 to serve as an assistant engineer on the Welland Canal. From 1845 to 1848 he was the engineer in charge of the construction of timber slides and river improvements on the Ottawa River at Bytown (now Ottawa). In 1853 his plans were accepted for an extensive water-supply system at Montreal, the first waterworks system designed by Keefer, who eventually became the most distinguished hydraulic engineer in Canada.

The first prize in the Hamilton competition was awarded to Samuel McElroy, an American engineer, but neither his plan nor any other of the submissions were used. Instead Keefer himself was commissioned in August 1855 to study all possible sources of water supply and submit his own plans for

1 Advertisement dated 16 September 1854, Hamilton *Spectator*, 18 September 1854.
2 Quoted in Paul Craven and Tom Traves, 'Canadian Railways as Manufacturers 1850-1880,' Canadian Historical Association *Historical Papers 1983* (Ottawa, 1984), p. 264.

a waterworks system. He recommended that the water be brought directly from Lake Ontario, rather than Burlington Bay, and then be pumped by steam engines to a distributing reservoir on high ground east of the city. Two eminent American engineers, John B. Jervis, who had designed and constructed the Croton Aqueduct which supplied New York City with 'pure and wholesome water', and Alfred W. Craven, then chief engineer of the Croton system, were consulted. They reported that *'the plan of pumping a supply from Lake Ontario, as recommended by Mr. Keefer, is regarded as the most simple . . . likely to be attended with the least ultimate cost, and capable of expansion as the wants of the city may require.'*[3]

On January 28, 1857, Thomas Keefer was engaged as Engineer by the newly appointed Board of Water Commissioners. In spite of the city's already considerable debt, and a financial depression that had taken place in the province after the end of the Crimean War in 1856, the Commissioners decided to proceed with the works, estimated to cost £147,000 ($590,000), a huge sum at the time. They expected the waterworks to give the city 'an important advantage over any other in Western Canada, and . . . induce a large proportion of those persons seeking residences, or situations for manufacturing establishments, to select this place in preference to others where good water cannot be obtained.'[4]

The site chosen for the pumping station was well outside the city limits at the time, and close to the lake shore where the filtering basin was to be located. The pumphouse was to be equipped with 'Woolf compound' steam engines of the type introduced in England about 1845 by James Simpson, then engineer to the Chelsea Waterworks Company. Simpson's rotative engine, with a controlling flywheel, represented the most advanced form of the beam pumping engine that had originated with Thomas Newcomen's 'atmospheric' engine,[5] the first recorded example of which was erected at a colliery near Dudley Castle in Staffordshire in 1712. The efficiency of the primitive Newcomen engine had been vastly improved by James Watt's invention of the separate condenser, which he patented in 1769. This was the first of Watt's many improvements to the beam engine. In 1782 he patented the double-acting engine, in which steam acted alternately on both sides of the piston, thereby doubling the power and providing a more even motion. To provide a rigid connection between the top of the piston rod and the beam, instead of the chain of earlier engines, Watt

3 *First Semi-Annual Report of the Water Commissioners for the City of Hamilton . . . 30th June, 1857* (Hamilton, 1857), p. 7.

4 Ibid., p. 14.

5 Steam was introduced below the piston and condensed by a jet of cold water. A partial vacuum was created, allowing atmospheric pressure acting on the top of the open cylinder to drive down the piston, thereby raising the pump rods and making a working stroke.

devised his famous 'parallel motion' to guide the piston rod in a straight line and minimize friction. In 1812 Richard Trevithick constructed the first 'Cornish engine', a condensing beam engine that worked at a much higher steam pressure than contemporary Watt engines to permit 'expansive' working[6] and dramatic savings in fuel. Arthur Woolf, also a Cornishman, had patented his compound engine eight years earlier, in 1804. This had two cylinders at the same end of the beam — steam entered the high-pressure cylinder and was exhausted into the low-pressure cylinder, where the steam continued to expand and work. The Woolf compound used even less fuel, but was more complicated and expensive than Trevithick's engine, and so was little used in Britain before the introduction of Simpson's rotative engine, which overcame the liability of the Cornish engine to wreck itself if it went out of control.

Both the waterwheels and pumps of the Montreal waterworks had been constructed in England. Keefer recommended that the Hamilton steam engines also be imported from Britain. 'If, however,' he wrote, 'the Commissioners decide to have the work done upon this side of the Atlantic, the attempt may as well be made in Canada as in the U.S., because no similar Engines have been built there, and because the duties, transportation, &c., would make the cost as great as if built in Canada.'[7] (As the *Scientific American* reported in 1864, 'double-cylinder expansive steam-engines' found little favour in the United States,[8] where the Cornish engine became the standard for waterworks for twenty years after its introduction at Buffalo, New York, in 1851. It was not until the 1870s that compounding slowly began to be accepted in America.)

Tenders were received for the pumping engines from D.C. Gunn of Hamilton and John Gartshore of Dundas. On September 10, 1857, Gartshore's tender was accepted. The tender was 'not only several thousand pounds lower than any other, but was payable wholly in Debentures.'[9] John Gartshore, a Scotsman, had immigrated to Canada in 1833. In 1838 he established his foundry in Dundas. His business flourished and he became the largest employer in the town. In 1862 it was reported that he manufactured 'all kinds of saw and grist mill machinery, wooden machinery, oil stills, worms, tanks, steam engines, boilers, burr stones &c. &c.' and that 'the average number of men employed is one hundred.'[10] Though John Gartshore has generally been credited with being responsible for the entire construction of the engines and

6 Steam was cut off early in the stroke so that it was completed by the expansion of the steam already in the cylinder.

7 *Second Semi-Annual Report of the Water Commissioners for the City of Hamilton . . . 31st December, 1857* (Hamilton, 1858), p. 5.

8 *Scientific American* 10 (9 April 1864): 232.

9 *Second Semi-Annual Report of the Water Commissioners*, p. 4.

10 *Journal of the Board of Arts and Manufacturers for Upper Canada* 2 (1862): 46.

pumps, except for the eye-bars of the parallel motion, the *Second Semi-Annual Report of the Water Commissioners* states that 'Mr. Gartshore is now importing the heavier and more important castings and forgings from abroad.'[11] The contract for the construction of the engine house, filtering basin by the lake, and the connecting conduit was awarded on February 18, 1858, to George Worthington, a Hamilton builder, the price again being payable in debentures.

By the end of June 1858 the two engines, except for the cylinders, were nearly ready for erection, according to Charles Robb, the 'Inspecting Engineer'.[12] A year later Keefer was able to report: 'The fitting up of the Cylinders and Connecting Rods is about all the important work remaining to be done to the machinery . . . I anticipate the completion of the whole work, so far as to be ready for use, sometime in September.'[13] The first engine was started on October 24, 1859, and three days later the first water was pumped to the Barton Reservoir; the second engine was started November 11. Each engine delivered 60,000 gallons of water per hour. The waterworks were officially inaugurated by the Prince of Wales in September 1860 during the first royal tour of North America.

The erection of the two massive engines was a major engineering task in itself. Unfortunately there is no contemporary account of this, and how, for example, the two huge walking beams, each 30 feet long and weighing 25 tons (plate 3-6), were raised into position on their bearings on the entablature or main beam 20 feet above the main floor. James McFarlane, who became the first resident stationary engineer at the pumphouse, was in charge of the erection for John Gartshore. McFarlane had immigrated to Canada from Scotland in 1854, and began working at Gartshore's Dundas Foundry about the time that work began there on the castings and forgings for the pumping engines. Two of his shopmates at the foundry were John Inglis, founder of the famous Toronto engineering firm, and John Bertram, founder of the equally well-known Dundas engineering firm; all worked on the Hamilton engines. In 1860 the Water Commissioners hired McFarlane to be Engineer in charge of the Engines. He remained in charge for fifty-one years, and brought up two families in the house allotted to him on the grounds of the waterworks.

Steam was originally supplied at the comparatively low pressure of 30 pounds per square inch by four Cornish boilers. The Cornish boiler, which was extensively used in Britain for large stationary power plants, had a single

11 *Second Semi-Annual Report of the Water Commissioners,* p. 4.
12 *Third Semi-Annual Report of the Water Commissioners for the City of Hamilton . . . 5th July 1858* (Hamilton, 1858), p. 6. Charles Robb, later a mining engineer and head of the Nova Scotia Geological Survey, is identified as the inspecting engineer in the *Canadian Illustrated News* 2 (Hamilton, 26 September 1863): 222.
13 *Fifth Semi-Annual Report of the Water Commissioners for the City of Hamilton . . . 17th October, 1859* (Hamilton, 1859), p. 7.

internal flue with the grate at one end; its design has been attributed with some uncertainty to Trevithick. The boilers, built by Gartshore, were 30 feet long and 6 feet in diameter; they weighed about 9 tons each, and consumed about 3,200 pounds of coal per day when working one engine. The 150-foot brick chimney of the pumphouse was required to produce an adequate draft to draw the fire through these boilers.

In 1881-82 the four Cornish boilers were replaced by two horizontal return-tube boilers which permitted the steam pressure to be doubled to 60 pounds per square inch, and higher still later. To accommodate these new boilers, the roof of the boiler house had to be raised, with little change, however, to its appearance. At the same time new pumps were put in place to greatly increase the capacity of the pumphouse. Both boilers and pumps were manufactured and installed by the local firm of Copp Brothers & Barry. These were only the first of a series of improvements and additions at the waterworks plant. An additional pumping station equipped with two horizontal cross-compound engines was built in 1887-88, and electrically driven pumps put into operation in 1909. After 1910 the old beam engines were left on standby, and from the 1920s until 1938 continued to be run once a year to maintain them in operating condition. The Gartshore engines were the pride of succeeding city engineers, who detailed staff to clean and polish them when men could be spared to do so.

A watercolour found among a collection of papers and drawings of Thomas S. Scott, the first chief architect of the federal Department of Public Works, appears to be a preliminary study for the pumphouse buildings (plate 3-7). There are differences between the rendering and the actual buildings — most noticeable is the lack of the flights of steps leading up to the main entrance of the engine house. The tall brick chimney is shown, somewhat attenuated, behind the boiler house instead of to the side as a separate structure, and the doors of the boiler house are located on the opposite side of the actual building. The remarkably sophisticated Italianate design of the pumphouse with its elaborate cornice and rusticated masonry suggests that Keefer could have had the assistance of an architect. It was common practice for engineers to call upon help with the aesthetic design of their structures — in England, Robert Stephenson employed Francis Thompson, and I.K. Brunel was assisted by Matthew Digby Wyatt. Scott, who was working in Montreal in the 1850s for the contractors constructing the Grand Trunk Railway, may well have met Keefer when the latter was engaged in the building of the Montreal waterworks. Whether the two men met or not, it is reasonable to surmise that Keefer had some professional assistance with the superb architectural design (plates 3-8 and 3-9).

The impressive monumental character of the Hamilton pumphouse is in striking contrast to that of the only other surviving installation of beam engines in North America, the pumping plant of the Chesapeake & Delaware Canal at Chesapeake City, Maryland. The stone buildings of the canal powerhouse in which the first surviving engine was erected in 1852 — it replaced an earlier engine dating from 1837 in a building adjoining the present pumphouse — are typical, severely plain, industrial structures with no architectural embellishments or pretensions. The engine, together with a second engine built in 1854, operated a massive 40-foot-diameter waterwheel to lift water into the canal.[14]

These engines provide another interesting contrast to the pumphouse at Hamilton, and reflect one of the many differences between American and British engineering practice. The parallel motion used so exclusively on beam engines of British manufacture, and superbly demonstrated in the Gartshore engines (plate 3-5), was rarely used in the United States. The canal powerhouse engines employ a pair of slide bars to guide the piston rod, with the crosshead connected by two links to the walking beam. James Watt wrote in later life to his son that he was more proud of his parallel motion than of any of his other inventions.[15] Its mechanical beauty seems to have so attracted British engineers that they never abandoned it for the simple crosshead and slide bars that were easier to construct with the development of the metal planer. (There are no plane surfaces in the parallel motion, and all parts could be forged, thereby facilitating their manufacture at the time of Watt's invention.) The Gartshore engines, though typical in almost every way of British design, nevertheless have one distinctly American feature: the trussing of the connecting rods. Such trussing was often used when the connecting rod was of considerable length to prevent bending or buckling of the cast-iron rod when under compression.

After the complete electric station opened in 1954, much of the earlier waterworks plant at the Hamilton Beach Pumping Station was slowly dismantled and many of the buildings demolished. The old pumphouse and its

14 Greville Bathe, 'The Lift Wheel Pumping Plant of the Chesapeake and Delaware Canal,' *An Engineer's Miscellany* (Philadelphia, 1938), pp. 101-116.
15 Rex Wailes, 'James Watt — Instrument Maker,' *Engineering Heritage*, Vol. 1 (London, 1963), p. 60.

engines remained, although the last series of steam boilers were removed. The publication of the book by William and Evelyn M. James on the waterworks and its historic pumphouse[16] created considerable local interest and spurred the creation of the 'Pump Group' by the Hamilton chapter of the Institute of Power Engineers. After more than three years work by this volunteer group, the 'north' engine was run in May 1982 under steam supplied from the nearby sewage treatment plant. On April 3, 1983, the pumphouse was opened to the public as the Hamilton Museum of Steam and Technology, which had been established the previous November by the Hamilton-Wentworth Regional Council, so that today visitors may inspect this finely preserved monument of Canada's industrial heritage.

16 William and Evelyn M. James, 'A Sufficient Quantity of Pure and Wholesome Water': The Story of Hamilton's Old Pumphouse (London, Ont., 1978).

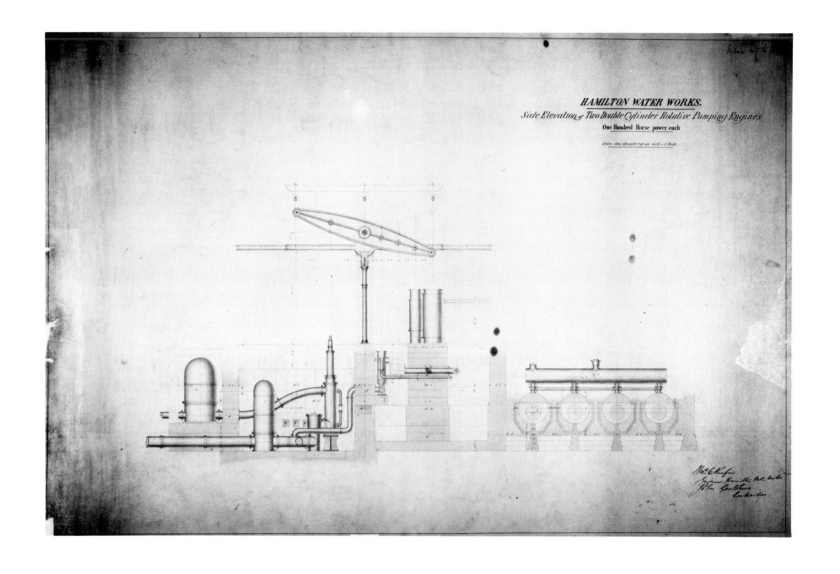

3-1 'Side Elevation of Two Double Cylinder Rotative Pumping Engines,' signed by Thomas C. Keefer and John Gartshore. *Mills Memorial Library, McMaster University*

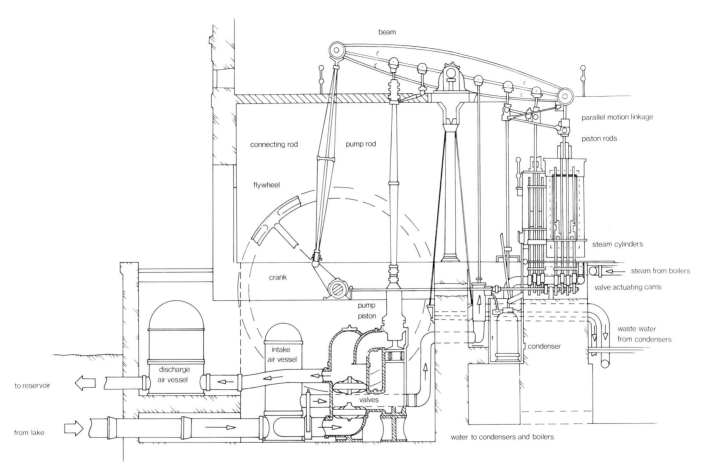

beam

parallel motion linkage

piston rods

connecting rod

pump rod

flywheel

steam cylinders

crank

steam from boilers

valve actuating cams

pump piston

waste water from condensers

intake air vessel

discharge air vessel

condenser

to reservoir

valves

from lake

water to condensers and boilers

GARTSHORE BEAM ENGINES

PARTS AND WATER CYCLE

3-2   Schematic drawing by Barbara Raymont. *Hamilton Museum of Steam & Technology*

3-3
From the *Canadian Illustrated News*, 26
September 1863. *Metropolitan Toronto
Library*

3-4
Main columns and one flywheel, 1977.

3-5
Top of one pair of high- and low-pressure cylinders, valve gear, and Watt parallel motion, 1977.

3-6   Pump and connecting-rod ends of walking beams, 1977.

3-7 'Engine House, Hamilton.' Undated watercolour, possibly by Thomas S. Scott. *National Archives of Canada* (C-107964)

3-8   From the *Canadian Illustrated News,* 26 September 1863. *Metropolitan Toronto Library*

3-9
Exterior view, 1986.

4

Gooderham & Worts Distillery, Toronto

The large-scale continuous processes characteristic of late-nineteenth-century production were successful first in industries processing liquids, such as sugar refining, brewing, and distilling. The change from batch to continuous production required not only technological innovations but also sophisticated plant design. This is well illustrated by the Gooderham & Worts distillery in Toronto, which ranks as this country's premier surviving example of the first generation of modern factory complex. It is also the earliest, most intact distillery operation still in use in North America.

The firm's history begins in 1831, when James Worts, a miller from England who headed a large family immigration to Upper Canada (Ontario), ordered the construction of a wind-powered flouring mill at the southeastern edge of the town of York, which three years later, in 1834, became the City of Toronto.[1] The half-acre site lay just west of the mouth of the Don River. In 1832 Worts's brother-in-law, William Gooderham, an English gentleman farmer, joined him to found the partnership of Worts & Gooderham. When Worts died unexpectedly in 1834, Gooderham continued in business under the firm name of William Gooderham, Company. In 1837 he added a whisky distillery, which was a natural outgrowth of flour milling to make efficient and profitable use of surplus and second-grade grain. Four years later, in 1841, he established a dairy farm adjacent to the distillery where the cattle were fed on the nutritious distillery by-product, 'spent wash'; this was a common business practice of nineteenth-century distillers (and brewers). Other physical improvements in the 1840s included converting the entire mill and distillery operation from wind to steam power and building a company wharf and grain elevator south of the plant. As for the windmill tower, 'on which the hopes and fortunes of the firm once rested, but whose machinery, dependent on the capricious, the wild, the weird gales of wind sweeping from Lake Ontario, could not be made by any human contrivance to work peaceably in the face of sudden tempests',[2] it remained in service for many years. Around it grew a tumble of small workshops for blacksmiths, coppersmiths, coopers, and carpenters, plus tanks, storage warehouses, stills, and a company office. Stables and cart sheds occupied other parts of the area (plate 4-1).

Gooderham's young orphaned nephew, James Gooderham Worts, joined him as a full partner in 1845. The firm's name was then changed to Gooderham & Worts, and the operation became known for a time as the Toronto City

---

1 Surprisingly little is known about this important family and its distillery business. See Dianne Newell, 'William Gooderham,' *Dictionary of Canadian Biography*, Vol. XI (Toronto, 1982), pp. 358-60, and in the same volume, Newell, 'James Gooderham Worts,' pp. 937-38; and H.L. Symons, *The Windmill, Notes and Digests from E.B. Shuttleworth's Book* (n.p., n.d.).

2 *Canadian Illustrated News* (Hamilton, C.W.), 25 April 1863.

Steam Mills and Distillery. Both men lived with their families on estates adjacent to the distillery. Worts devoted most of his efforts to managing the distilling and milling business, which experienced remarkable growth.

By the 1850s Toronto was becoming the dominant urban centre in Canada West (Ontario), and serviced a flourishing agricultural hinterland. These were the great days of wheat-growing in the province; it was not until the late 1860s that competition from the American West began to be felt. For many farmers the sale of grain to a distiller meant cash and prosperity. Railway construction in this decade greatly improved transportation, while lake shipping remained as important as in earlier days. The Gooderham & Worts distillery, located on the harbour in the heart of the city's new industrial district and alongside the newly constructed Grand Trunk Railway, grew to become an industrial showplace and make its owners the city's largest taxpayers.

What stands on Gooderham & Worts site in 1988 represents the period of major building expansion between 1859 and 1890. It began with construction of a rather severe-looking 4½-storey structure of Kingston limestone to house an integrated distillery and flour milling operation. This is the oldest structure standing on the site today. Like the original windmill, the new distillery, running east and west parallel to the shore of the lake, became a landmark on the Toronto waterfront. The new distillery, old windmill tower (with the auxiliary structures removed), and William Gooderham's large house, stables, and a lawn and orchard located just northwest of the distillery occupied a 3-acre block bounded to the north by Mill Street, on the west by Parliament, and on the east by Trinity. The site across Trinity, running east to Cherry, was completely taken up by the firm's 9-acre dairy farm, where several thousand cattle were fed in rows of company-owned sheds, which are shown on the Boulton map of 1858 (plate 4-2). The firm's expansion was not surprising; in the words of business historian Alfred Chandler, Jr., 'Only after the grain-growing regions had expanded and ancillary storage facilities permitted high-volume year-round operation did demand for the large automatic mill appear.'[3]

Construction of the rock-faced limestone ashlar distillery and mill building began in 1859 under the direction of the Toronto engineer and architect, David Roberts, Sr. The structure consists of the 4½-storey main building of limestone, a 1½-storey section also of limestone, and an extended red-brick section of one storey. The design of the main building is in the simplified

3 Alfred Chandler, *The Visible Hand: The Managerial Revolution in American Business* (Cambridge, Mass., 1977), pp. 250-251.

classical tradition of British industrial architecture of the early nineteenth century (plate 4-3). Only the curious pediment above the single projecting bay on the south face, and the fact that this bay is set off-centre, betrays the later date of this remarkably fine structure, which is 300 feet long and 80 feet wide. The stone walls measure 3½ feet thick; thick cast-iron columns 12 inches in diameter support the floors. Roberts insisted on a double thickness of wooden beams and 18-inch-thick rafters; these rested on stone mounts so as not to pull down the walls if a fire occurred. His design also required the workmen to string a network of wrought-iron rods across the interior of the building and bolt them to the heavy exterior walls to keep the walls from spreading. Although the interior was totally gutted in an explosion and fire on October 26, 1869, thanks to the architect's foresight and the firefighters' skills, the outer walls of this fire-resistant factory remained standing. One reporter on the scene used these words to describe the effect of the spectacular 7-hour fire on the distillery: 'From the nature of the building, the amount of woodwork in the interior was immense, and the timber of the most massive kind, and as a result it took a long time to destroy it . . . . The massive iron pillars by which the different floors were fastained [sic], placed one above the other with rafters eighteen inches between remained long in their positions, but as the rafters were gradually consumed, the pillars toppled down one after the other, adding to the intensity of the awful ruin within. The iron rods which ran across the building in all directions, supporting the walls, snapped and this was a fresh source of anxiety . . . . The wall cracked and went in various directions and the top of the east gable was so twisted that every moment it was expected to topple.'[4]

The distillery was rebuilt immediately and equipped in the original manner. When completed early in 1861, it produced 6,000 gallons of spirits per day, making it the largest distillery operation in Canada West. Flour and grist milling continued but only as a subsidiary activity to distilling. A local newspaperman estimated the cost of the new buildings and equipment, which included an engine house, a range of storehouses, and modern machinery and stills for the old windmill tower, at $200,000.[5] The works had required upwards of 500 labourers and mechanics to complete.

Roberts designed the combination distillery and flour mill to be entirely

4 Toronto *Globe*, 27 October 1869.
5 Ibid.

mechanized yet use the principle of gravity-flow. It was a highly functional building in which much evidence of the original process remains visible today. In the tall section, with its gable end facing Trinity Street, raw grain — half a million bushels annually — was converted into whisky by being ground, soaked, cooked, fermented, and distilled. The most common grains used in producing whisky are barley, corn, and rye; the proportion and type of grain used determines the whisky type. Gooderham & Worts produced what would become a Canadian specialty: rye whisky.

The grain supplies from as far west as Chicago arrived by railway (the firm had a private siding for 14 railcars) and lake steamer.[6] In the distillery, ingenious devices moved grain and other products from area to area, floor to floor, and section to section. An elevator or enclosed endless belt with small lifters attached carried the various types of grain from the temporary subterranean storage bins located in the eastern, milling end of the distillery to the top of the building; from there the grain dropped through metal spouts into the hoppers of the grinding millstones on the 'stone floor'; there were eight millstones in all. Set directly on the floor below the millstones was the wheelroom containing the mechanism for rotating them (plates 4-6 and 4-7). It would appear that the wheelroom attracted many visitors who were curious about and fascinated by the new machinery of the age. 'These wheels, spurs and pinions, horizontal and vertical shafts,' wrote a journalist for the *Canadian Illustrated News*, 'all work as smoothly as a happy family; their swift, soft motion is like music.'[7] A powerful 100-h.p. beam engine manufactured by Baillet & Gilbert of Montreal drove the millstone mechanism and the various devices for moving grain and other products throughout the building.[8] The engine stood on the same floor as the wheelroom but was concealed in a separate fireproof compartment of dressed stonework. And, as was typical of the stationary steam engine in its factory role, it was entirely separate from its boilers, which were located in the northeast corner of the main building.

Mashing and fermenting occurred next. Once ground in the mill, the grain (meal) descended in covered spouts through the wheelroom, then travelled in elevators up to the fourth floor of the next section of the building. Each elevator delivered its contents into one of several bins arranged in rows. The attendants drew off a specific mix of meal into a line of travelling bins, the contents of which the workmen would release into the mouth of a hopper in

6 Unless otherwise stated, the description of the construction and original milling and distilling processes is taken from *Canadian Illustrated News*, 25 April 1863, and Toronto *Globe*, 27 October 1869. Information about the later changes is based mainly on an interpretation of the various fire insurance plans of the site and discussions with Gooderham & Worts Ltd. personnel and Stephen Otto.
7 *Canadian Illustrated News*, 25 April 1863.
8 Reported in the Toronto *Globe*, 7 February 1862, and *Canadian Illustrated News*, 25 April 1863. The *Globe*, 11 July 1859, named the firm as Barclay & Gilbert.

the mashroom below on the third floor. Mashing involves the crucial step of controlled-temperature cooking of a mixture of meal and crushed malt in hot water. Malt is processed barley; the enzymes that are part of the malt dissolve in water to convert the starch of the grain into a sugary liquid known in distilling (and brewing) as 'worts'. The Gooderham & Worts plant operated four copper-lined mechanical mashtubs; each measured 15 feet in circumference, 7 feet in depth. Pumps then drew the mash of grain from the kettles automatically. The mash travelled downwards along metal troughs to the fermenting cellar located in the 1½-storey structure adjoining the main building. In metal vats called fermenters, attendants added yeast to convert the fermentable sugars in the mash to alcohol or spirit. Fermentation posed a bit of a bottleneck in the process, for it took several days to complete. Over the years, when the firm wished to increase production, it had to increase the number or capacity of the fermenters. Finally, pumps forced the fermented mash, commonly known as 'beer', back into the main structure to the stillroom, located in the attic, where the alcohol was separated from the mash.

The still installed at the new Gooderham & Worts plant represented the latest in a nineteenth-century development: a continuous or column still. This evolved from Aeneas Coffey's British patent still of the 1830s and was a great improvement over the old batch process using the traditional pot-still.[9] The continuous still at Gooderham & Worts rose 40 feet through the third and fourth floors. The fermented mash fed in continuously from the top, flowed down a column of perforated plates, and mixed with the vapour of steam coming up from the bottom. The alcohol in the mash vapourized and flowed into a condenser. In the condenser, the alcohol vapours rose through a series of perforated chambers and condensed in cooling to a fluid. Three elevated circular receivers collected the spirits, while a separate large, square chamber at the base of the still received the spent wash, which emptied through a series of spouts and travelled out of the building and under Trinity Street to a tank located near the cattle sheds, where it was dried for feed.

All mixtures of alcohol and water are known generally as spirits. The spirits produced in the first distillation are a weak product known in distilling as 'low wines'. After filtering or leaching this product in tall wooden rectifying vats containing charcoal (there were 42 of them located on floors 3 and 4), workmen poured or racked the spirits into the aging barrels. Leaching was a

9 William L. Downward, *Dictionary of the History of the American Brewing and Distilling Industries* (Westport, Conn. 1980), pp. 182-83.

common practice amongst whisky distillers in the nineteenth century but was abandoned in the twentieth. After being stored and ripened for anywhere from two months to a year, the product sold throughout the province as 'common whisky'. Distilling a second time (termed 'doubling') however, produced a higher quality of spirit; this the firm sold throughout North America and abroad as 'old rye' or 'toddy whisky'. Until the mid-1860s the second distillation would occur in the windmill tower, which Roberts had ordered fitted up with two copper pot-stills of 1,500 gallons each.

The final, essential step in the manufacture of whisky is aging. Whisky is clear and colourless before maturation; during aging, the spirits extract and absorb colours and flavours from the wood barrel, taking on a reddish-amber colour and a characteristic flavour. Whisky ages anywhere from a few months to many years, depending on consumer tastes and official regulations. Spirits were and are, however, subject to government excise tax at the point of manufacture. As a financial concession to distillers, in the nineteenth century governments developed the practice of permitting distillers to store spirits during aging in a supervised or bonded warehouse for a stated period of time tax-free. At the new Gooderham & Worts plant the bonded warehouse and storehouse areas were located in the 1½-storey section, in areas adjacent to and above the fermenting cellar. These areas would soon prove too small for the task once productivity levels rose. The one-storey brick tail section of the distillery housed the cooperage for repairing and cleaning the barrels used for aging and those returned by customers. The company cooperage for making new barrels was located a half mile to the north, in the block bounded by Front, Cherry, Water, and Market (in the 1880s renamed Worts) streets.[10] Later the company converted the cooperage section of the distillery into additional fermenting rooms. Because of the aging requirements and because whisky was sold in barrels rather than bottles until the end of the nineteenth century, distilleries employed large numbers of coopers; in 1863, 40 of them worked for Gooderham & Worts.

David Roberts, Sr., perhaps in association with the prominent architectural firm of Gundry and Langley, designed the next new structure built on the site: the massive maltings and storage building (1863-64) running north of the east end of the distillery and mill building (plate 4-11).[11] Like most of the other buildings constructed on the site at the same time and over the next few

10 *Canadian Illustrated News*, 25 April 1863; and Charles E. Goad, *Atlas of the City of Toronto and Suburbs, 1884*, plate 29, Ontario Archives, O.S. 15; and Goad, *Atlas of the City of Toronto and Vicinity, 1890*, plate 29, Ontario Archives, O.S. 14.
11 Toronto *Globe*, 26 March 1863, and information from Stephen Otto.

decades, it was constructed of red brick on a rock-faced limestone ashlar foundation; the brick piers and corbelling at the eaves are not merely decorative but serve to strengthen the load-bearing walls, which in the maltings have comparatively small windows.

To produce malt, grain (usually barley) is steeped in water, encouraged to germinate to a certain point, then dried and roasted to halt the process. The work was closely supervised by a maltster. In the traditional floor-malting or 'couching' operation, such as the one introduced at Gooderham & Worts in the 1860s, skilled workmen spread a quantity of soaked grain to a specified thickness on the paved floors of the maltings and allowed it to germinate. They then shovelled the germinating grain by hand at frequent intervals for consistency. Accordingly, the ceilings of the maltings were very low to provide more floor surface for the operation. Likewise, a proliferation of small, closely spaced window openings provided the necessary ventilation. The floors rested upon cast-iron columns. The product, known as 'green' malt, was kiln dried by roasting for several days in the final stage of the malting process. All these structural features — low ceilings, many small windows, and a kiln tower carrying rooftop ventilators — were typical of nineteenth-century maltings and gave them a very distinctive exterior character. Entirely new, mechanized forms of malting in combination with pressured air-drying began to be introduced in the 1870s and 1880s. By the twentieth century, these made floor-malting obsolete and meant that the production of malt came to be done primarily by independent companies. Today, examples of the modern linked silo-like tower maltings operated by independent companies can be seen elsewhere along the Toronto waterfront.

In the main portion of the Gooderham & Worts maltings, five brick vaults divided the first floor longitudinally for storing spirits. Malting took place on the second and third floors. The high attic storey served as storage for the raw barley.[12] Malt was kiln dried in the stove-like tower built at the north end; tall decorative ventilators — one oval, the other square — with arched windows topped the tower (only the square cupola remains). In the basement were the furnaces (west half) and malt storage bins. Green malt entered the kiln through iron-shuttered openings at the tower end of the two germinating floors. Hot air circulated under the roasting malt as it was dumped from one perforated iron floor to the next. The kiln-dried malt ended up in the distillery

12 Goad, *Insurance Plan of the City of Toronto, 1880 revised to 1889*, Vol. 1, sheet 11, block 37, Metro Toronto Central Library.

building, where it was crushed in rollers before either being used by the company to make its whisky or sold commercially to others. Although the floor-malting method became obsolete by the turn of the century, the firm continued producing malt in this facility until World War I.

The other structures constructed at this time, adjacent to the maltings, were a 2½-storey storehouse with a cooper's shop on the first floor, a 3-storey alcohol tower, and a large 3-storey office building, all attached. The Gooderham & Worts office building occupies the old windmill-tower site between the maltings and the east end of the distillery building. In the rear portion of the office building is the attractive 3-storey alcohol tower topped by a highly decorative, glazed cupola. While the original purpose of the tower is not entirely clear, it eventually became a company salesroom for entertaining clients.

By the early 1870s Gooderham & Worts was producing one-third the total amount of proof spirits distilled in Canada; family members also were financially involved in banks, flour mills, and stores outside Toronto, and the two local narrow-gauge railways, the Toronto, Grey & Bruce and the Toronto & Nipissing.[13] The Gooderham & Worts commercial interests were the latter railway's main customer, and the Toronto terminal of this line was established conveniently near the distillery. In this decade and the next, Gooderham & Worts constructed a new distillery building across Trinity Street on the site of the old cattle sheds, the so-called 'pure spirits' building, a large central steam plant, and a string of alcohol storehouses and warehouses. As for the cattle-feeding operation, the firm shifted it to a site a short distance away, south of the line of the Grand Trunk and Toronto & Nipissing railways on the east bank of the Don River, in an area known as Riverside.[14] (As a result of the straightening of the Don in the 1870s, the new course of the river ran further east than previously.) Both Gooderham and Worts died in the 1880s, leaving million-dollar estates; their business holdings were left to their sons, George William Gooderham, Jr., and James Gooderham Worts, Jr., who together completed the expansion phase for the distillery operation. George became president and his son, Albert Edward, vice-president and managing director.

Construction of the pure spirits building across the street from the company offices began in 1873.[15] Here, neutral spirits, a tasteless and odourless, highly inflammable alcoholic product which is distilled at a very high proof from a

13 Canada, Parliament, *Sessional Papers* (1876), III No. 3; and 'Canadian Railways, No. XXV: Toronto and Nipissing Railway,' *Engineering: An Illustrated Weekly Journal* (London) 28 (July–December 1879): 295–98 (this source is not completely reliable).

14 See Goad, *Insurance Plan of the City of Toronto, Ontario 1880, revised to 1889*, Vol. 2, sheet 90 (March 1882); and the photograph, 'Gooderham & Worts Ltd.,' Toronto, 16 December 1918, National Archives, PA-96856. By the 1880s, with the introduction of refrigerated railway cars, the company began fattening beef cattle which it then slaughtered and exported to English markets.

15 Toronto *Globe*, 5 June 1873.

mash of any fermentable material, was produced for use as a base for making gin, vodka, cordials (artificial liquors), and blended whisky. Blended whisky was a new Gooderham & Worts product made possible by the introduction of the continuous still. Though the company manufactured many of these products itself, it also sold large quantities of the raw alcohol for the manufacture of vinegar, methylated spirits, and the scent 'Florida Water'.[16]

The pure spirits building has changed little over the years except for the addition of a fourth storey to the south end section, thus destroying the symmetry of the elevation facing Trinity Street (plate 4-12). The facade is almost entirely glazed between five plain brick piers which rise above the roof. The ornamental iron railing on the narrow balcony above the ground floor is most unusual for an industrial building (while the large cupola which once crowned the roof, though in keeping with the earlier buildings on the site, seemed out-of-style on this building of almost modern appearance). The extensive glazing was highly practical, for it formed 'blow-out' walls. If an explosion were to occur in one of the stillrooms, the shock waves would destroy the glass rather than the brick supporting walls; thus, the building would remain standing. Flanking the 4-storey central section which contained stills were two 3-storey spirits storage sections. Next to the pure spirits building, just to the north of it, the company built a 1-storey cart house (which after 1900 became a garage) and the large central steam plant with its imposing 173-foot brick chimney.

The majority of the buildings occupying the rest of the 3-block site were the massive multi-storey warehouses constructed in the 1870s and 1880s for storing spirits in tanks ('tank houses'), aging spirits in barrels ('rack houses'), and flavouring, colouring, and blending spirits ('denaturing department'). In the 1890s tank and rack houses also were built on the north side of Mill Street, on the site of the old Worts estate.[17] The architect responsible for designing most of the new structures in the 1880s and 1890s was David Roberts, Jr.[18] These brick warehouses were once hives of activity. As many as two dozen men and several horse-drawn wagons attended to the warehouses, hoisting the barrels of spirits from floor to floor using block and tackle and muscle power. Crews of inspectors combed the warehouses constantly checking for leaking barrels. Most of these solid old structures still stand, though not all remain in company hands.

16 'Canadian Railways No. XXV: Toronto and Nipissing Railway.'
17 The spacious Worts estate complete with mansion shows up on the insurance plan by Goad, *Atlas of the City of Toronto and Vicinity, 1890*, plate 29. However, Goad's *Insurance Plan of the City of Toronto, 1880, revised 1889*, Vol. 1, sheet 11, block 36, shows the Worts mansion slated as 'to be pulled down'.
18 Information from Stephen Otto. David Roberts, Jr., signed the plans for the 6-storey rack house at Trinity and Mill streets.

During World War I and Canada's brief period of prohibition, which continued piecemeal for a few years after the war, all distilleries ceased producing alcoholic beverages. Gooderham & Worts converted its entire distilling operation to the manufacture of acetone, a highly inflammable component of the smokeless explosive cordite, also the production of anti-freeze.[19] British Acetones, Toronto, Ltd., the name under which the company operated in this period, adapted many of the storage and other buildings for use as stillrooms, and it constructed a compressor house and an anti-freeze canning factory. Other, more permanent changes occurred to the site at the end of the war as a result of the city's large-scale harbour reclamation project. The company had to dismantle the old Gooderham & Worts wharf as well as the grain elevator and coal storage facilities (plate 4-9), and the Gooderham & Worts operation, along with its neighbours, found itself completely landlocked.

The first major permanent changes as far as the distillery operation was concerned occurred in the 1920s, when Gooderham & Worts ceased to be a family-owned business and the operation entered a gradual and continual decline. The 1920s were marked by big business concentration in Canada. A Whitby, Ontario, man named Harry C. Hatch with his associates bought the Gooderham & Worts company in 1923, though a nephew of George Gooderham, Edward Douglas Gooderham, who had been associated with Gooderham & Worts since 1902, remained a director of the firm until his death in 1950.[20] Hatch then bought a second major and equally venerable Canadian distilling operation, Hiram Walker & Sons Ltd., from the Walker family in 1926. In 1927 Hatch merged the two companies under the parent company of Hiram Walker-Gooderham & Worts Ltd. Because of the excellent reputation of the Hiram Walker brand of rye whisky, 'Canadian Club', the new company decided to concentrate its Canadian whisky distilling operations at the Hiram Walker plant in Walkerville (Windsor).

Small amounts of Gooderham & Worts brand whisky and rum (distilled from molasses) as well as anti-freeze continued to be manufactured at the Gooderham & Worts division plant until the 1950s. Under the new ownership, further changes were made to the site.[21] Rum production, which involved a much more simple process than whisky production, required the installation of several steel molasses tanks at the west end of the distillery. The obsolete

19 The Ontario Temperance Act of 1916 prohibited the sale or consumption of spirits in the province. Federal prohibition, invoked as a war measure in 1918, ended with the war. The provinces began repealing provincial prohibition in 1919 but Ontario waited until 1927.

20 *Industrial Canada* v. 68 (May 1967), pp. 205-7; and 'Capsule History of Hiram Walker' (typescript prepared by the Public Relations Department, Hiram Walker-Gooderham & Worts Ltd., Walkerville, Ontario, 2 March 1964). Hiram Walker, a successful Detroit businessman and grain dealer, built a flour mill and distillery on the Canadian side of the Detroit River in 1857, at a place which became known as Walkerville. Little evidence of the early operation remains, though the luxurious company office building (1894) designed by the celebrated Detroit automobile-industry architect, Alfred Kahn, is essentially unaltered and still being used for executive offices.

21 Underwriters Survey Bureau, *Insurance Plan of the City of Toronto, 1948*, Vol. 1A, sheets 10 and 11, Ontario Archives.

one-storey cooperage-turned-fermentation floor in the distillery provided a convenient heated storage facility for one of them. Elsewhere on the site the company converted the old central steam plant of 1886 into a maintenance and repair facility. It left the idle chimney standing but later had to remove the top half as a safety measure. Malt production ceased altogether and the old maltings became used for racking operations and drum storage. Most of the remaining buildings, other than the warehouses, were no longer needed even for storage purposes. In spite of this, the company left most of the buildings standing and, due mainly to the traditional character of the distillery business and the historically-minded staff and management at the Gooderham & Worts site, it has maintained them.

Once prohibition ended in the United States in 1933, Hiram Walker-Gooderham & Worts Ltd. quickly became the world operation that it is today, and in the economic boom following World War II, the parent company decided to expand the Walkerville operation. As a result, in 1957 it stopped production of rye whisky and anti-freeze at the Gooderham & Worts site in Toronto. Because the milling operation and much of the distilling capacity of the Gooderham & Worts plant was no longer needed, the company scrapped some of the equipment, including the distillery steam engine (by that year, 1957, a 375 h.p. engine was in use). Nevertheless, the old distillery still bears much physical evidence of the milling and whisky-distilling process, even of the steam engine operation. The distillery's 100-foot ornamental brick chimney of 1859-61 still stands and at full height. Also, the shells of the old coal-fired furnaces and remnants of the perforated floor sections of the kiln are still to be found in the basement of the long-abandoned maltings tower.

In the two decades following World War II, the entire industrial district of which Gooderham & Worts was a major part faced abandonment. Although many of the old plants remained there, the industrial expansion spurred by World War II caused a great number of firms to shift their factory production to the urban rim. Also, an elevated expressway constructed just south of the distillery parallel to the rail line added greatly to the general isolation of the older district. Because of the heavy investment in the bonding and storage facilities at the Gooderham & Worts site and the fact that Metropolitan Toronto is the largest single market in Canada for Hiram Walker-Gooderham & Worts Ltd. distilled products, the company has maintained a small rum-distilling operation there. Only by continuing to distill in Toronto could the company keep its licence to operate these bonded storage facilities.

Recently, the parent company has shown an interest in the heritage value of the old plant. Accordingly, in 1985-86 it rehabilitated the 1870s cart house/parking garage for office use by personnel of the Gooderham & Worts Ltd. division. The former company offices and alcohol tower (now known as the 'cooper room') that date from the 1860s were sensitively remodelled as the new Toronto offices of Hiram Walker & Sons Ltd. Company officers also began investigating the feasibility of reactivating some of the old distilling and milling equipment. In spite of these encouraging signs, however, the future for the Gooderham & Worts complex is not secure, for in 1986 the British conglomerate Allied-Lyons bought out Hiram Walker-Gooderham & Worts Ltd. The Allied-Lyons organization has a good reputation for supporting heritage projects in Great Britain, and it is hoped it will recognize and respect the Toronto complex as an outstanding heritage resource in Canada.

4-1   The windmill tower, by William Armstrong, c. 1855. *Gooderham & Worts Ltd.*

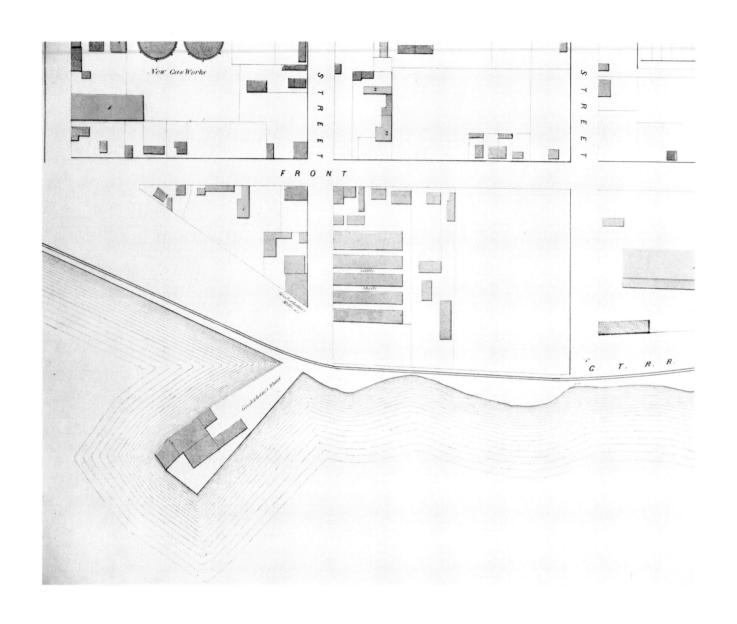

4-2   Section from plate 29, *Atlas of the City of Toronto,* by W.S. & H.C. Boulton, 1858.
Metropolitan Toronto Library

4-3   The distillery, from the *Canadian Illustrated News*, 25 April 1863. *Metropolitan Toronto Library*

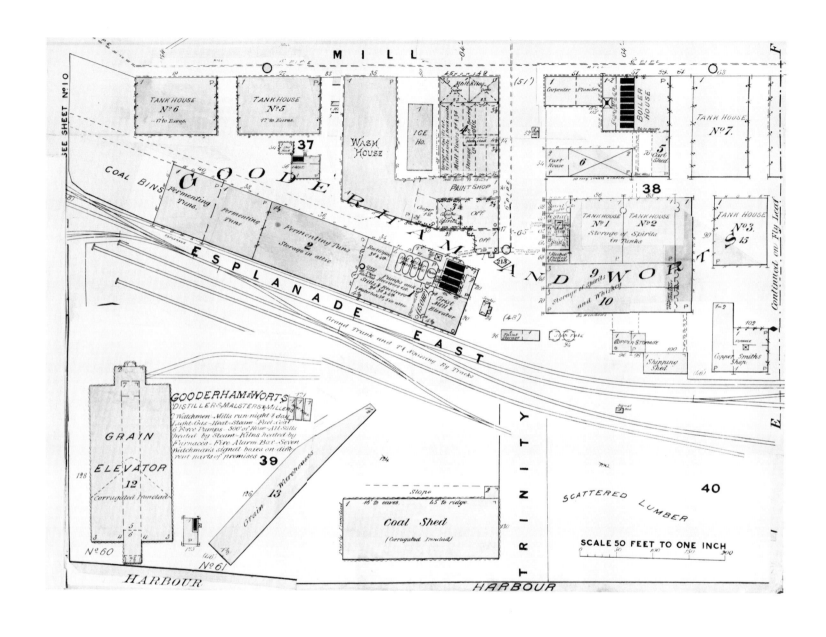

4-4   Section from sheet 11, *Goad Insurance Plan of Toronto . . . 1880, revised 1889. Metropolitan Toronto Library*

4-5   Chromolithograph from a view by A.H. Hider, 1896. *Royal Ontario Museum, Toronto*

4-6   Millstone machinery, from the *Canadian Illustrated News*, 25 April 1863. *Metropolitan Toronto Library*

4-7   'Mill — Ground Floor — Stonehurst,' 12 November 1918. *City of Toronto Archives*

4-8   Rye whisky bottle 'bottled in bond under excise supervision 1908' (ht. 31 cm.).
Dianne Newell/Arts Audio-Visual Services, University of B.C.

4-9   The elevator, 19 November 1918. *City of Toronto Archives*

4-10   The distillery from the railway yards, 1987.

4-11
The maltings, 1987.

4-12
The pure spirits building, 1988.

5

Belt and Line-Shafting Transmission of Power

Toward the middle of the nineteenth century in North America, simple water-powered milling (a pre-industrial process for isolated and local production) gave way to steam- or water-powered factory production; a major difference between the former and the latter was the method and scale of power transmission. When the belt main drive that originated in New England was combined with the British system of high-speed shafting during the second half of the nineteenth century, the result was the development of a sophisticated transmission technology. The employment of a steam engine or hydraulic turbine as the factory prime mover, connected to the machinery by belting and line shafting, has now been superseded by the use of individual electric motors. Nevertheless there are some remarkable examples of the survival until recently, and even today, of the nineteenth-century system.

The ordinary water mill, such as the village grist mill, sawmill, or fulling mill, performed operations that were simple and repetitive. The waterwheel was directly connected to the machinery by either wooden gearing or a connecting rod and crank on the wheelshaft. The industrial mill or factory required a quite different system. It housed a variety of operations, and an elaborate mechanical layout was needed to convey power from the waterwheel, steam engine, or hydraulic turbine to the various machines throughout the plant. The function of the transmission system was not only to distribute power to all sections of the plant, but also 'to subdivide the aggregate power into such parcels of energy as were required to place each machine, large or small, in motion at the rotating speeds required for the operation or operations performed.'[1]

In the mills and factories of the late eighteenth and early nineteenth centuries, the power source was connected to the machinery by wooden shafting running on iron journals and driven by wooden gearing. This ponderous and slow-moving system was soon replaced by cast-iron gearing and shafting developed in England during the first decade of the nineteenth century. The substitution of cast iron for wood in the wheelwork was a considerable improvement, although the system was still relatively inefficient (to overcome the brittle nature of cast iron, the castings had to be large and heavy).

Beginning in 1815, the famous British engineering partnership of William Fairbairn and James Lillie pioneered the shift from cast-iron to wrought-iron shafting. The adoption of the much lighter wrought-iron shafting, together

1 Louis C. Hunter, *A History of Industrial Power in the United States, 1780-1930*, Vol. 1, *Waterpower in the Century of the Steam Engine* (Charlottesville, Va., 1979), p. 418.

with the redesign of the hangers, couplings, and pulleys, achieved not only a major reduction in the mass of the millwork but a substantial increase in rotational speeds. Since higher shaft speeds are capable of delivering more power, these developments greatly improved mechanical efficiency. However, the shafting was still directly geared to the power source and involved the use of extremely heavy vertical main shafts. The problems created by such heavy vertical shafting could be seen at the great Saltaire Mills completed in 1853 (plate 5-1). As Fairbairn himself reported: '[In this woollen mill] the vertical shaft is 10 inches diameter through the first two rooms, 8½ inches through the third room, and 6½ inches to the top; the velocity being 94 revolutions per minute . . . . Great trouble is sometimes experienced with the foot of the vertical shaft, which from its weight and the great pressure upon it, has a tendency to heat, unless sufficient bearing-area is allowed and the parts kept thoroughly lubricated.'[2]

In the United States a new method of transmission was being developed in the form of belt drive directly from the prime mover. It was at the newly built large-scale Appleton Mills at Lowell, Massachusetts, in 1828 that belting was first adapted to the main drive to do away with the heavy English-type system found in all other American mills at the time. Endless bands, straps, or belts made of gut, rope, leather, or canvas had, of course, been used in the earliest factories for connection from the gear-driven countershafts, but until the Appleton Mills went into production, belting had never been used to drive the line shafting itself. Although the original belt-drive system developed for Appleton Mills required much improvement, nevertheless it ran far more smoothly and quietly, cost less, and was more easily installed and repaired than the traditional gear drive.

Tightly stretched belts were standard when Ithamar Beard published a paper in 1837 advocating loose-running belts.[3] The advantages of slack belts became apparent with the adoption of British high-speed shafting; frictional losses were reduced and there were fewer breakages. By 1860 the improved belt drive was the common form of power transmission in use throughout North America. The introduction about this time of lighter and more true cold-rolled shafting, at first of wrought iron and later of low-carbon steel, further improved the rotational speeds and efficiency of belt transmission. (Rotational speeds were determined by the ratio between the diameter of the

2 William Fairbairn, *Treatise on Mills and Millwork, Part II. On Machinery of Transmission and the Construction and Arrangement of Mills*, second edition (London, 1865), p. 105.

3 Theodore Z. Penn, 'Development of the Leather Belt Main Drive,' *IA: The Journal of the Society for Industrial Archaeology* 7, 1 (1981): 6-7.

drive pulley and that of the driven pulley; the greater the power requirements of the machine, the wider the belt and pulleys needed.) Europeans were slow to relinquish gear drives, but 'by 1900, the practice of the "American System" was becoming general'[4] in both Britain and the Continent.

The chief difficulty encountered with the line shafting lay in the necessity to maintain the proper alignment of both shafting and bearings. The settling of a mill's foundations, or the shrinking and warping of its wooden framing, could play havoc. Several machinists independently 'invented' the universal hanger with self-aligning bearings to counteract this problem (plate 5-2). The production not only of line shafting but of its many components became a major industry; in Canada the Dodge Manufacturing Company of Toronto was one company specializing in the manufacture of transmission systems (plate 5-3). Another industry was the production of belting itself and the equipment needed to repair and service it: belt tighteners, clamps, awls, punches, laces, etc.(plate 5-4).

The small, water-powered, belt-driven mill of the Mundell Lumber Co. in Erin is the last water-powered mill in operation in the Credit Valley watershed and a rare example of its type. The West Credit River was a source of power for a succession of mills in this tiny village located northeast of Guelph. At the south end of the village, the river drops 25 feet beneath Main Street. A local pioneer by the name of Daniel McMillan both purchased and built a series of mills to use the power beginning in 1835. His first two operations were sawmills. On land across the road from the mill by the Charles Street dam, he built a grist mill close to the lower course of the river — today the Mundell Lumber Co. planing mill.[5] McMillan received a 999-year lease on water rights for the saw and grist mills in 1847; then, in search of a higher head of water, he received permission from the Council of the District of Wellington in 1849 to construct a millrace from the Charles Street dam across Main Street to his grist mill (plate 5-7).[6] McMillan built a second grist mill, powered by a millrace from the Church Street dam upriver, in 1849[7], but unfortunately died that same year.

Upon his death, McMillan's first grist mill and, importantly, the long-term lease on water rights passed through several hands before Ben Mundell bought the old mill in 1896 for a planing mill and lumber business. Today the

4 Hunter, *History of Industrial Power*, p. 472.
5 *Mainstreet: A Pictorial History of Erin Village* (Erin, 1980), pp. 5-7, 11.
6 Indenture dated September 1, 1896, shown to me by Terry Mundell.
7 By-law passed by District Council, District of Wellington, February 10, 1849.

enterprise, including a modern hardware store on Main Street, is operated by Jim and Bill Mundell, brothers who are the third generation to own the business, and their sons. Together they manage the 'back section', the sawmill and planing mill where the lumber is custom finished. Mundell's employs two men full time in the mill, one of whom is apprenticing to take over the operation from a long-time employee with over 30 years service.

The planing mill retains and still uses turn-of-the-century woodworking machines (rip saw, band saw, thickness planer, boring machine, and sticker for specialty mouldings and trims), all of them belt-driven at speeds between 1,200 and 2,500 r.p.m. Other machines, such as a sander and a tenoner, have survived but are not being used. The old painted and decorated machinery was manufactured in the province at foundries in Galt (MacGregor & Gourlay & Co. and Cowan & Co. of Galt Ltd.[8]) and Preston and Toronto (J.R. Williams & Co. Ltd.). The equipment on the ground floor of the mill remains as it was in the 1890s, operated by water power. The waterwheel is kept in use because it is somewhat of a 'free good'. And there is no problem with water supply, because the company controls the hydraulic system, including the Charles Street dam. The hydraulic system with its turbine requires minimal maintenance and operates reliably, even on cold winter days when ice must be chopped away from the water gate. Because the machines on the second floor are used more frequently than those on the first, it has become more convenient to use a small electric motor to power a second shaft of pulleys on the ground floor to drive the equipment on the floor above.

The water-powered transmission system is quite simple to operate. On the ground floor, a turn of a wheel opens the water gate below. Water flowing via the headrace from the millpond across the street hits the small reaction turbine (horizontal waterwheel), causing it to rotate. (The hydraulic turbine came into its own in the 1850s. Not only did it deliver a much greater percentage of the potential waterpower than did the traditional vertical waterwheel, but, unlike the latter, it was not affected by seasonal variations in water level.) As the turbine, which develops approximately 15 h.p., begins turning, it operates a canvas belt from a pulley on its shaft. The belt drives another pulley located on the main shaft with several other pulleys, each of which is capable of driving a machine on the floor above (plates 5-8 and 5-9). The machine operator can engage or disengage a specific machine from the line shafting by

8 'Catalogue No. 9, Galt Machine Works, Cant, Gourlay & Co., proprietors,' 1882, and sheets from 'Catalogue No. 10, Cowan & Co., Galt Foundry, Engine and Machine Works, Galt, Ontario,' (n.d.), can be found in the National Archives, Archives Library Division, John Davis Barnett Collection, MG 30, B 86, Vol. 32.

moving a wooden lever which slides the moving belt from an idler pulley onto a drive pulley located beside it on the same countershaft. The unmistakable low rumbling and gentle slapping sounds typical of belt and line-shafting transmission can be heard throughout the mill.

It is possible to maintain and repair the old mill's belt transmission system in spite of the system being long obsolete. The Mundells run the belts fairly slack, as is common practice. According to a standard handbook on power transmission, 'more power may be transmitted . . . by increasing the tension, but this is accompanied by the disadvantage of requiring extra attention and undue pressure upon bearings.'[9] To be properly maintained, belts must be replaced frequently. Mundell's has both the equipment and experienced staff to do its own belt lacing. When belts do wear out at Mundell's, they are easily replaced from the stocks of belt dealers in Toronto and Mississauga, who are in business mainly to supply belting to Ontario farmers for their belt-driven farm machinery. Unlike belts, however, pulleys are no longer being manufactured. The Mundells have overcome this potential problem by stockpiling old pulleys acquired from abandoned belt-driven operations throughout the region.

Most other lumber and builders' supply businesses in Ontario are in the mass-demand market, and deal in standard sizes for doors, window frames, stair rails, and other wooden items. The demand for off-sizes or special features is usually met by carpenters. Because it retained the old belt-driven woodworking machinery, Mundell's is one of the few lumber and builders' supply businesses in the province that can produce custom work by machine. Consequently, its customers come from every corner of southern Ontario. At a time when the restoration of older buildings is becoming increasingly popular, the Mundells, fortunately, are not about to change their ways.

An example of the survival until recently of the use of belt-driven factory power in a large-scale, modern manufacturing plant is Fittings Limited, 136 Bruce Street, Oshawa, which was established in 1902 as a stove foundry.[10] With the growth of manufacturing in Oshawa after World War I, the company later specialized in the production of pipe fittings, at first of grey iron and later of malleable iron. It soon became the largest malleable iron foundry in Canada, with 14 acres under roof on a 22-acre lot near the centre of town. In addition to pipe fittings, the company produced custom castings of all kinds,

9 Hubert E. Collins, *The Power Handbooks. Shafting, Pulleys, Belting and Rope Transmission* (New York, 1908), p. 132.
10 The information on Fittings Ltd. was supplied to Ralph Greenhill by Gordon Ridout, Oshawa, and Edward Storey, Port Perry.

including castings for the automotive and railway industries. In spite of modernization a few years earlier, the plant closed down in June 1987. There had been a decline in sales, but the plant was now totally operated by electricity and the company was unable to obtain its power at an economical price; the high property taxes on the site in downtown Oshawa were also a factor in the decision to close down.

The tapping floor where the castings were machined was the foundation of the company. It was originally powered by a steam engine. The conversion of the tapping floor to electricity simply involved the replacement of the steam engine by an electric motor, with the line shafting and belting remaining in use until the end of production (plate 5-5).

The experience with belt transmission at the Oil Well Supply Co. Ltd. works on Robert Street in Petrolia presents a somewhat different, yet more typical, story — with the imperative need for most industries to modernize to survive, only the occasional piece (if any) of old equipment powered from line shafting is still useful. Oil Well Supply dates back to the discovery of the Petrolia oil fields in the 1860s. A percussion drilling technique using a walking beam and solid wooden drill rods operated by steam power plants was introduced to the Ontario oil fields at Petrolia about 1866 to replace spring poles operated by manpower. The man who developed and promoted the pole-tool drilling rig in the pioneer Ontario petroleum industry was a local businessman, William H. MacGarvey.[11] With the Canadian system, long-grained hardwood boring rods about 2 inches in diameter were used instead of the manila rope typically employed in the early American cable tool system.

While the 'Canadian System' of drilling pioneered by MacGarvey was suited to the shallow-lying oil fields in this region, the system required several local innovations to be practical. For example, at each level in sinking a well a skilled driller employed successively smaller drill bits, easing and speeding his progress. To fit iron casings into the lower and smaller dimension drill hold, a collarless casing was developed. The end of the pipe was enlarged slightly in order that the succeeding length of pipe might be threaded to it. The single source for this 'belled' pipe was the Oil Well Supply Company of Petrolia.[12]

As Petrolia drillers moved away to newly opening oil fields in Eastern Europe, Australia, and elsewhere in the 1870s and 1880s, the Oil Well Supply

11 Dianne Newell, *Technology on the Frontier: Mining in Old Ontario* (Vancouver, 1986), pp. 35-36, 128, 130.
12 Charles Whipp and Edward Phelps, compl., *Petrolia, 1866-1966* (Petrolia, 1966), p. 61.

Company furnished the percussion drilling rigs and tools for drilling, casing, and recovering tools and lengths of pipe in the hole ('fishing' tools). After the consolidation of the original company with a local rival firm in 1890, the new company of the same name became deeply engaged in the manufacture of all manner of supplies for oil, salt, gas, and artesian wells, plus tools and machinery for deep-well boring.[13] It was for a time the largest drilling supply manufacturer and exporter in Canada and, because it is still in business in its original location and plant, may be the oldest producer of oil-well drilling tools in the world.[14]

Today Oil Well Supply Company Ltd. serves the southwestern Ontario market almost exclusively. In 1979 motor-driven (originally steam-driven) line shafting and belting still powered several machine tools in the factory, including the century-old gap-bed lathe by McKechnie & Bertram, Dundas, Ontario, shown in plate 5-6. Then a few years ago the company replaced its belt-driven machine tools with expensive electrically operated, automatic equipment. Drilling water wells (and to a lesser extent, oil, gas, and salt wells) in southwestern Ontario is a large, competitive business, and the Oil Well Supply Co. felt it had no choice but to modernize.

13 Toronto *Globe*, 24 June 1893.
14 J. Wilson, D. Wilson, and W. Moon, 'Oil, Sweat, and Tears' (typescript teaching kit produced in co-operation with Petrolia Discovery, Petrolia, c. 1980), appendix A.

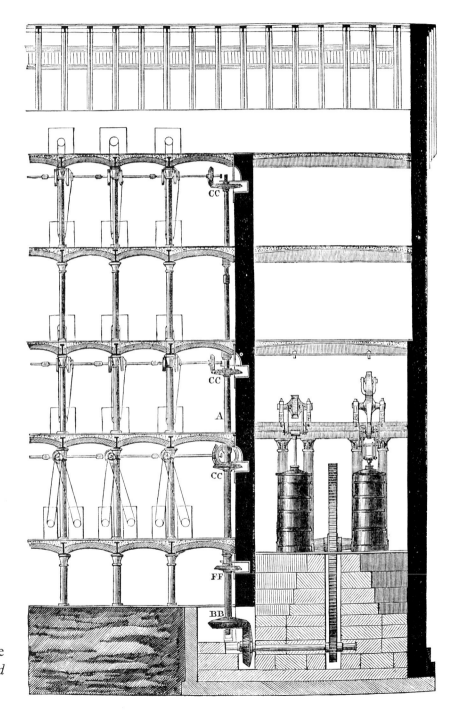

5-1
Main drive by vertical shafting and gearing, Saltaire
Mills, from William Fairbairn, *Treatise on Mills and
Millwork, Part II,* London, 1865.

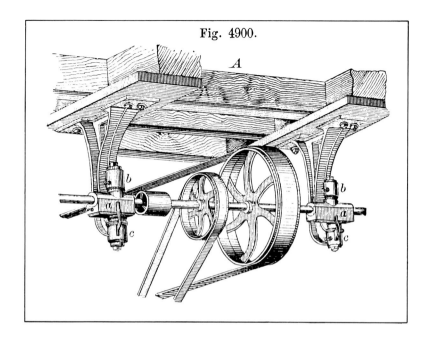

Fig. 4900.

5-2

Countershaft with universal hangers, from *Knight's American Mechanical Dictionary*, Vol. III, New York, 1876. 'The journal box *a* is held between two pintles or stems *b c*, the ends of which are concave, those of the box bearing being convex so as to form a species of ball and socket joint, and allow the box to adjust itself to the alignment of the shaft. The box is self-lubricating; the oil, after being drawn up from a reservoir below by the rotation of the shaft, and performing its office, is again returned to the reservoir, the drip-cup being dispensed with.'

Adjustable Ball and Socket Hangers.

With Standard Bearings.

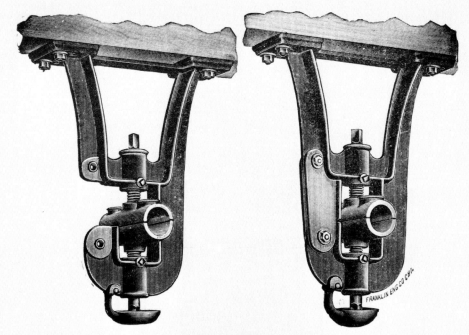

SINGLE AND DOUBLE BRACE.

These Hangers are the same as our capillary and chain oiling patterns as far as the frames are concerned, and have the double brace links when desired; but the bearings are not fitted with any automatic oiling device, but are intended for use with grease or oil.

These Bearings may be used with a ball of waste saturated with oil, in each cup at the top, or with grease, either in a loose form, in candles or in compression grease cups.

PATENT BELT TIGHTENER,

FOR DRAWING BELTS TOGETHER FOR THE PURPOSE OF LACING THEM.

This apparatus has proved itself indispensable to every establishment using belts of six inches wide and upward, and will soon pay its cost in the saving of time in lacing belts, much quicker and better than any other way, and avoids any necessity or excuse for injuring a wide belt by putting it upon the pulleys after it is sewed.

DIRECTIONS FOR USING.

Turn back the thumb screws sufficiently to allow the eccentric to go well on the bed-piece; bring down the thumb screws carefully so as to get an even bearing on each edge of the belt, and all is ready to work the crank. Should it be necessary to slacken one edge of the belt, carefully turn back the thumb screw on that edge, and when sufficiently slackened put down the screw again and proceed until the desired tightness is obtained. If the machine is properly applied, the operation is perfect, and there is no possible failure.

Size,	-	6	8	10	12	14	16	18	20	22	24	26	30
Price, each,		$15	$16	$18	$20	$22	$23	$25	$26	$28	$30	$34	$36

BELT AWLS.

Cast Steel blades, Black Ebony finished Handles, per doz., - - - - - - - $1 50

PALMER'S PATENT BELT AWL.

Made from best Cast Steel, each blade carefully hardened and tempered.
The point is so constructed that it is easy to pierce any thickness of belt. The body of the blade is made like a hollow reamer, and will easily cut a clean hole from ⅛ to ⅜ inch.
Put up in one dozen boxes, per doz., - - - - - $5 00

BELT PUNCHES.

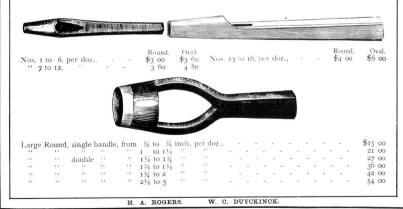

		Round.	Oval.			Round.	Oval.
Nos. 1 to 6, per doz.,	- - -	$3 00	$3 60	Nos. 13 to 16, per doz.,	- -	$4 00	$6 00
" 7 to 12,	"	3 60	4 80				

Large Round, single handle, from ½ to ⅞ inch, per doz.,	- - - - - - -	$15 00
" " " " 1 to 1⅛ " "	- - - - - - -	21 00
" " double " 1⅛ to 1¼ " "	- - - - -	27 00
" " " " 1⅜ to 1⅝ " "	- - - - - - -	36 00
" " " " 1¾ to 2 " "	- - - - - - -	42 00
" " " " 2⅛ to 3 " "	- - - - - - -	54 00

H. A. ROGERS.   W. C. DUYCKINCK.

5-4
From a catalogue dated 1 June 1872.

5-5
Tapping floor, Fittings Ltd., Oshawa, 1978.

5-6
Gap-bed lathe by McKechnie &
Bertram, Dundas, Oil Well Supply
Co.Ltd., Petrolia, 1979.

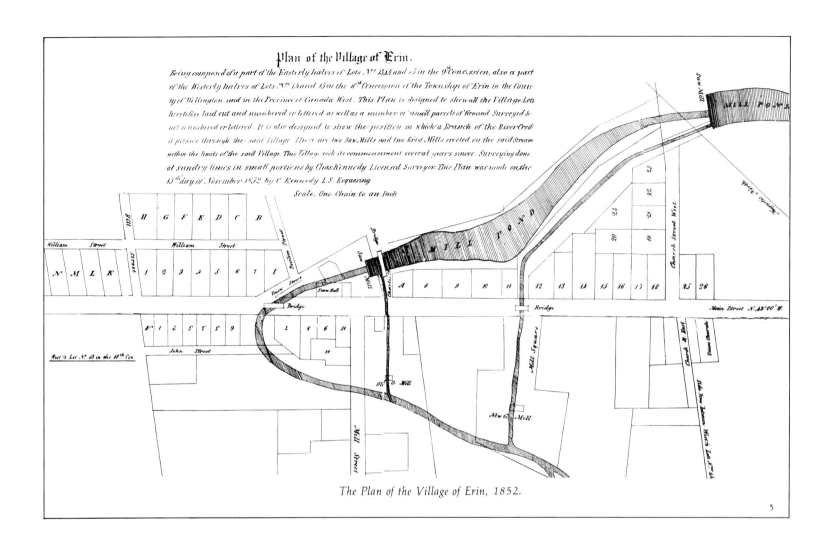

The Plan of the Village of Erin, 1852.

5-7   Plan of the village of Erin by Charles Kennedy, 15 November 1852.

5-8   Main shaft (the main pulley with drive from the turbine is 4th from right), Mundell Lumber Co. Ltd., Erin, 1987.

5-9
Thickness planer, Mundell Lumber
Co. Ltd., Erin, 1987.

The Ontario oil fields, together with those in Pennsylvania, were the first in the world to be exploited on a commercial scale, beginning in 1859-60. Within a few years of their development the Ontario fields were being worked by an ingenious mechanical system introduced to simultaneously pump dozens of petroleum wells using only a single small-powered engine. Today, about 75 percent of the approximately 400 wells in the Oil Springs, Ontario, field continue to be pumped with the primitive technology which has undergone little modification.

The Ontario petroleum region lies at the western end of the St. Lawrence lowlands, in a district which is geologically comprised of undisturbed limestone and Paleozoic strata rich in fossils, overlaid by drift clays, sands, and more recent surface deposits. Except where cut by rivers, it is a remarkably flat country of prime agricultural land. At the time of the oil discoveries, it was only thinly forested. The most commercially valuable petroleum deposits occurred in two distinct areas in Lambton County, mainly in Enniskillen Township. The first important discoveries were near what became the Village of Oil Springs (plate 6-1). The Oil Springs field extended over a small area 2½ miles by 1 mile, and was at a depth of fewer than 400 feet. Petrolia was the second, more extensive field; it stretched 13 miles by 2 miles and was only slightly deeper. The average thickness of the original reservoir in both cases was a mere 10 feet. (Oilmen also found crude oil in other localities over a much wider area, only not in the paying quantities needed to sustain development.) Thus, the Ontario oil fields were doomed to be of marginal significance when they faced competition from increasing numbers of new and larger oil fields elsewhere in the world. The Ontario oil fields are of considerable importance, however, in terms of their technological developments.

The novelty and peculiarities of petroleum, such as its inflammability, and the practical need to process the petroleum fully because its market was largely domestic, called for a host of technological inventions and innovations to overcome the problems of drilling and pumping, of refining and by-product recovery, of safe storage and transportation, and of developing new uses to enhance its commercial potential.[1] At first it was only the middle fraction of distillation, kerosene used as lamp oil, that was a highly marketable product. There was almost no demand for the first product of distillation, naphtha, and though a little of the residue was used as fuel or for lubrication, most of the

6

The Jerker System for Pumping Oil, Lambton County

1 Dianne Newell, " 'All in a Day's Work': Local Innovation on the Ontario Mining Frontier,' *Technology and Culture* 26, 4 (October 1985): 799-814.

latter was waste and simply dumped.

Because of local experimentation and innovative activity, Ontario was able, in petroleum technology, to make important contributions at an international level of both skilled labour and special technology — the 'Canadian System' of drilling (the drilling technique using solid wooden poles) and the Frasch process of refining and deodorizing petroleum being the most significant examples of the latter. Not all technology developed in the Ontario oil fields was commercially marketable of course. The wooden 'jerker' system introduced to pump the oil wells experienced a long-term popularity in this region that seems to have occurred nowhere else.

Some information about the first techniques for drilling and pumping petroleum is available from old newspaper accounts and testimonies presented to the Ontario Royal Commission on Mineral Resources.[2] The oilmen detected oil-bearing strata from surface gum beds and springs, then tapped into them by digging ordinary wide-bore water wells through the clay to a depth of about 40 to 80 feet to the rock below. These surface wells were 4 to 5 feet in diameter, with sides cribbed to prevent them from collapsing. The drillers tapped the deeper-lying strata by boring, using artesian-well techniques, several hundred feet into the shales and rock beneath the drift clay. Penetrating the deeper-lying strata revealed a surprise: the great spontaneously flowing region. A government geologist, Robert Bell, who visited the oil region in 1862, reported that 'the trunks of trees, over a considerable extent of low ground, were blackened to a height of several feet by the oil which had temporarily flooded the neighbourhood.'[3] The gushers quickly diminished or ceased altogether, whereupon the oil had to be pumped to the surface. The oilmen used the ancient method of spring poles operated by body weight to both drill and pump the earliest wells. Water power was not an option, as it was unavailable to the oilmen given the local topography of the region. They had to replace the spring-pole method about 1863 and reach the deeper levels by steam-powered drilling and pumping units.

At first a separate steam engine supplied power to each well, but as the number of wells increased and production began to fall off between 1863 and 1865, the relative scarcity of steam engines in this newly developing region, plus the high cost of purchasing and operating them in terms of fuel and labour, likely inspired a drive for a more practical power system. Some

2 Ontario, *Royal Commission on the Mineral Resources of Ontario and Measures for Their Development* (Toronto, 1890).

3 Robert Bell, 'The Petroleum Fields of Ontario,' *Proceedings and Transactions of the Royal Society of Canada* 5 (1888): 102.

improvisations using a single steam engine to pump two wells, to operate a sawmill and pump a well, or to use the same engine to pump one well and drill another, occurred. However, the real solution to subdividing the steam engine's power to distribute it around the oil field occurred only with the introduction in about 1863 of the wooden jerker system, whereby a steam engine of about 12 h.p. was able to run 20 to 70, or even 90, oil pumps over several acres of ground. This was accomplished by a simple contrivance of flat wooden rods (to transmit power from the pumping engine to the wells), bell cranks and horizontal iron wheels (to change the direction of transmission in the field), and walking beams (to connect the transmission lines with the pump rods in the wells).

It seems that John H. Fairbank was the first Oil Springs operator to use the jerker transmission system successfully on a large scale, though his biographer points out that Fairbank seems not to have considered this achievement important enough to note in his diary, which otherwise is very thorough.[4] Fairbank and his contemporaries reported to the provincial royal commission a few decades later that the system was unique — even a 'local invention' — but it was not.[5] The same technique was in use in Europe in the seventeenth century, if not before. What little information we have about the origins of this system is the result of studying old coins and engravings.[6]

The forerunner of the jerker system, called the *Stangenkunst* (roughly translated as 'rod work with crank'), was likely introduced into the German mining areas of Central Europe in the mid-sixteenth century. These were the mining areas and the years Agricola describes in his classic treatise *De Re Metallica* (1556), without however mentioning the *Stangenkunst* principle or name. This early mine-pumping system consisted of a piston pump driven through a crank and an extended horizontal series of reciprocating flat wooden rods (*Feldstagen*) by a waterwheel located at a distant point from the mine. The rods moved in opposite directions in double lines, parallel to the ground, with rocking arms supporting them. Where necessary, a horizontal wooden lever in the shape of a cross (*Kunstkreuz*) changed, at right angles only, the direction of power transmission. The original system met with refinements during the seventeenth century, and its use spread. Fine depictions of the *Stangenkunst* exist in a series of elaborately detailed mining landscapes on seventeenth-century German coins (plate 6-2), and in engravings such as that of de Fer

4 Edward Phelps, 'John Henry Fairbank of Petrolia (1841-1914)' (Master's thesis, University of Western Ontario, 1965), p. 30.

5 *Ontario Royal Commission on Mineral Resources*, pp. 157, 159.

6 Robert P. Multhauf, 'Mine Pumping in Agricola's Time and Later,' *United States National Museum Bulletin* 218, Paper 7 (1959): 114-20.

(1705), as depicted in plate 6-3. Later a version of the *Stangenkunst* for mine-pumping purposes was used with the great Laxey waterwheel on the Isle of Man beginning in 1854. Here, tiny wheels which ran along the ground on rails supported the wooden transmission rods from below.[7]

It is possible that the *Stangenkunst* was occasionally applied to other operations in mining, such as ore dressing. J.J. Brown writes of seeing in the Deutsches Museum in Munich a model of a medieval iron mine in which a waterwheel and system of jerker rods powered the crushing machinery.[8] Yet it seems unlikely that the *Stangenkunst* would have been structurally tough enough for this type of work. The main feature, and real advantage, of the system lay in the cheapness of its operation over long distances when the power requirement was low, such as for pumping.

Once the steam engine (itself introduced in the eighteenth century to pump water from mines) came into widespread use in the nineteenth century as a more reliable, portable, all-season prime mover, a system was eventually devised in which the steam engine was adapted to power *Stangenkunsten* pumps. (There was a serious disadvantage in depending on a waterwheel — which was such an unreliable and geographically limited prime mover — for the critical operation of removing water from deep mines: if the pumps stopped operating unintentionally, underground work would cease and possibly miners' lives could be lost.) With the adoption of the steam engine, the *Stangenkunsten* method was suited to the requirements of the Ontario and Pennsylvania oilmen who were searching for a cheap and practical source of pumping power. It is not known how they learned of the *Stangenkunst*, but certainly the principle was a simple one to imitate.

In order to pump many oil wells and still keep fuel requirements, hence operating costs, at a minimum in Ontario, the system underwent several modifications to reduce friction along the line. There exists one written account of early experiments with the *Stangenkunst* (referred to in the oil region as the jerker system) after its introduction into the Ontario oil fields by J.H. Fairbank. Fairbank testified before the provincial Royal Commission of 1888-89 that the jerker system 'was first used with a horizontal walking beam, that was afterwards improved by using a wheel, with which there is a great deal less friction. I think (the Englishman) Mr. Reynolds was the first who introduced the wheel.'[9] The horizontal 'spider' or field wheel, to which

7 Frank D. Woodhall, *Steam Engines and Waterwheels: A Pictorial Study of Some Early Mining Machines* (Ashbourne, England, 1975), p. 14.
8 J.J. Brown, *Ideas in Exile: A History of Canadian Invention* (Toronto, 1967), pp. 67.
9 *Ontario Royal Commission on Mineral Resources*, p. 159.

Fairbank referred, operated in a rotary reciprocating motion both to change the direction of transmission and to subdivide the prime mover's power among many pumps (plates 6-7 and 6-8). The operators achieved flexibility by attaching the rods at points along the perimeter of the field wheel so as to direct the transmission at a variety of angles. No one at the time of its adoption in Ontario bothered to describe the jerker system in any detail, though a John Tracy drew the fascinating bird's-eye view of it shown in plate 6-4. Wells in the Oil Springs field are still pumped by the old method. Today it is possible to see the extent to which the jerker system embodied the *Stangenkunsten* principle, and also the degree to which that principle has been advanced in the Ontario oil fields.

A typical pumping rig is shown in plate 6-6. A small electric motor is belted to a countershaft, and this in turn is belted to the large bullwheel which both acts as a flywheel to even out the motion and reduces the speed and increases the power. A pinion gear on the bullwheel shaft drives two spur gears, which further reduce the speed and increase the power. Each spur gear drives two cranks set at 180 degrees. The four cranks are connected to pitman arms, which convert the continuous rotary motion of the bullwheel shaft to the linear reciprocating motion of the jerker rods. Each pair of pitman arms is connected to a main field wheel located outside the engine house.

The largest pumping rig ever built for the jerker rod system, the Fitzgerald rig, which still exists in part and continues to work at the Petrolia Discovery museum field, is belt-driven. When it was erected in 1903, it was powered by a steam engine (plates 6-10 and 6-11), but today, like the gear-driven multiple pumping rigs, an electric motor powers the single surviving bullwheel. The Fitzgerald rig was designed to do contract pumping, but went into bankruptcy after a couple of years, partly because of the permanent decline of the Petrolia field. Nevertheless it continued to operate with only a few periods of idleness, and today is the only surviving belt-driven rig except for a very small operation at Bothwell.

The reciprocating motion of double rigid lines of flat wooden jerker rods transmits power from the pumping rig to the oil wells. These rods are hung from cedar posts by light iron hangers. Each well is coupled to the main transmission system by a single line connected to the free end of a balanced walking beam by a chain and pulley (plate 6-9) or a metal triangle arm. At the other end of the walking beam hangs the pump rod, whose weight furnishes the alternate pull on the jerker line. The whole assemblage works to and fro with each stroke of the pumping rig with a maximum stroke of 3 feet.

The original transmission system, still in use on the largest property in the Oil Springs field, the J.H. Fairbank Estate (owned by Charles Fairbank, great-grandson of the pioneer oilman), is constructed almost entirely of wood, and therefore is light, inexpensive, and easy to repair. The light construction is possible because at no time is the system under compression, only tension. It is arranged to be in balance, half the dead load of rods and mechanism in the field being lifted while the other half descends. The power required is only that for overcoming inertia and friction, plus the weight of the oil lifted at each stroke. Careful balance has been achieved by running a second set of rods off the opposite end of the engine to counterbalance the original set. Most strikingly, parts for the jerker system can be manufactured on the site easily and economically — and the equipment can be repaired locally.

The system used in the Ontario oil fields represents only an intermediate refinement in a long line of development of the *Stangenkunst* principle. In the oil fields of Pennsylvania, which quickly became a world centre of petroleum production, oilmen soon replaced the wooden jerker system with more powerful (but also more expensive) versions needed for the much deeper wells. These were constructed entirely or iron or steel and employed steel cables and/or iron rods in place of wooden rods. A modified version of the Pennsylvania system is now being used in the Oil Springs field by Morningstar Oil Producers, who are also making use of an alternate form of multiple pumping, a vertical eccentric 'pumping power' acquired from second-hand sources in Pennsylvania (plate 6-13). The system needs less maintenance, and the equipment is more available and costs less to set up.

During the late nineteenth and early twentieth centuries, American oil well suppliers marketed versions of the Pennsylvania system to various countries, including Japan. Examples of three separate versions of the Pennsylvania multiple pumping systems continue in use today in the Kanatsu oil fields, which are located near the Japanese city of Niitsu.[10] In England there is a remarkable surviving example of an entire layout of flat iron rods, driven by a waterwheel, at the site of the old Wheal Martyn Clay Works in Cornwall.[11] The last of the iron rod systems to work in Britain fell into disuse following World

10 Hiroshi Imai, 'To Search for the Roots of Pumping Power' (trans.), *Industry and Culture* [Niigata Industrial Archaeology Society, Japan] 1 (1978): 26-48.
11 Woodall, *Steam Engines and Waterwheels*, pp. 14-19.

War II, but similar systems remained in use in Germany as late as 1965.[12]

The low capital cost and operating efficiency of the jerker system made it possible to continue to work the shallow wells at Oil Springs, which after 1880 yielded only a few barrels of oil per day. By 1886 the average production per well per day in the entire Oil Springs-Petrolia region (which included approximately 2,600 producing wells) was under half a barrel.[13] In the same year, the average number of pumping engines at work in the district was 75, or one to every 35 wells; the engines had an average of 18 h.p. This represented quite a change from the boom years of a few decades earlier, when the flowing wells of Oil Springs and Petrolia yielded over 1,000 barrels each per day.[14] Production in the twentieth century continued to decline, during which time the gas engine, then the electric motor, replaced the steam engine as a prime mover for the jerker system. The new sources of cheap energy permitted the owners of oil properties to continue to work their wells and supply the local refinery at Sarnia.[15] It is not difficult to see why, in circumstances of marginal productivity and widely fluctuating prices for crude oil, the pumping technology of the nineteenth century has continued in use to the present day.

12 Ibid., p. 19.
13 Bell, 'Petroleum Fields,' pp. 111-12.
14 R.P. Charbonnier, et. al., *Analysis and Characteristics of Oil Samples from Ontario* (Ottawa, 1969), pp. 64, 79.

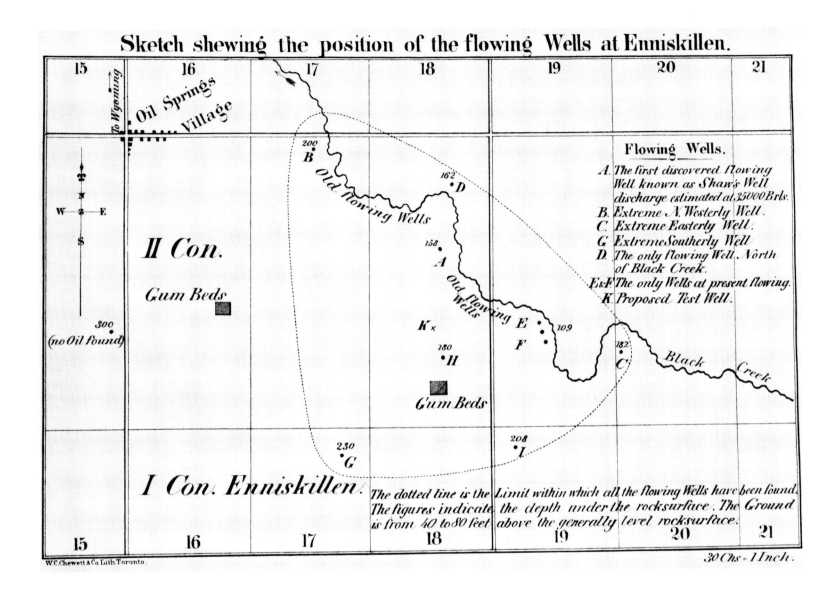

Sketch shewing the position of the flowing Wells at Enniskillen.

Flowing Wells.

A. The first discovered flowing Well known as Shaw's Well discharge estimated at 25000 Brls.
B. Extreme N. Westerly Well.
C. Extreme Easterly Well.
G. Extreme Southerly Well.
D. The only flowing Well, North of Black Creek.
E & F. The only Wells at present flowing.
K. Proposed Test Well.

The dotted line is the Limit within which all the flowing Wells have been found. The figures indicate the depth under the rocksurface. The Ground is from 40 to 80 feet above the generally level rocksurface.

II Con.

I Con. Enniskillen.

Gum Beds

Gum Beds

Oil Springs Village

Old flowing Wells

Old flowing Wells

Black Creek

To Wyoming

W.C.Chewett & Co Lith Toronto.

30 Chs = 1 Inch.

6-2   Brunswick 3½ taler, depicting *Stangenkunsten* pumps (in their typical conical shaft-houses) powered by an overshot waterwheel, 1677. *National Museum of American History, Smithsonian Institution*

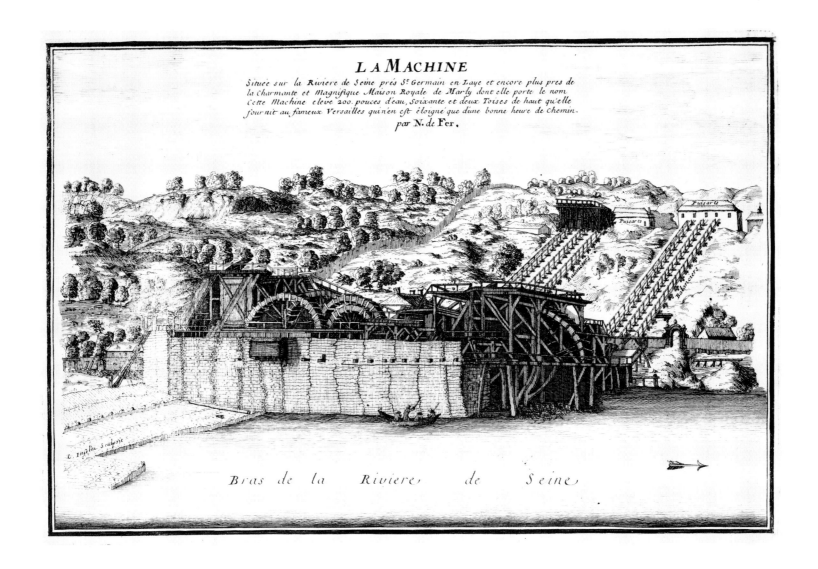

LA MACHINE

Située sur la Riviere de Seine prés St. Germain en Laye et encore plus pres de la charmante et Magnifique Maison Royale de Marly dont elle porte le nom. Cette Machine eleve 200. pouces d'eau, Soixante et deux Toises de haut qu'elle fournit au fameux Versailles qui n'en est éloigné que d'une bonne heure de chemin.

par N. de Fer.

Bras de la Riviere de Seine

6-3   The waterworks at Marly, built to supply the fountains at the Palace of Versailles, by N. de Fer, 1705.
National Museum of American History, Smithsonian Institution

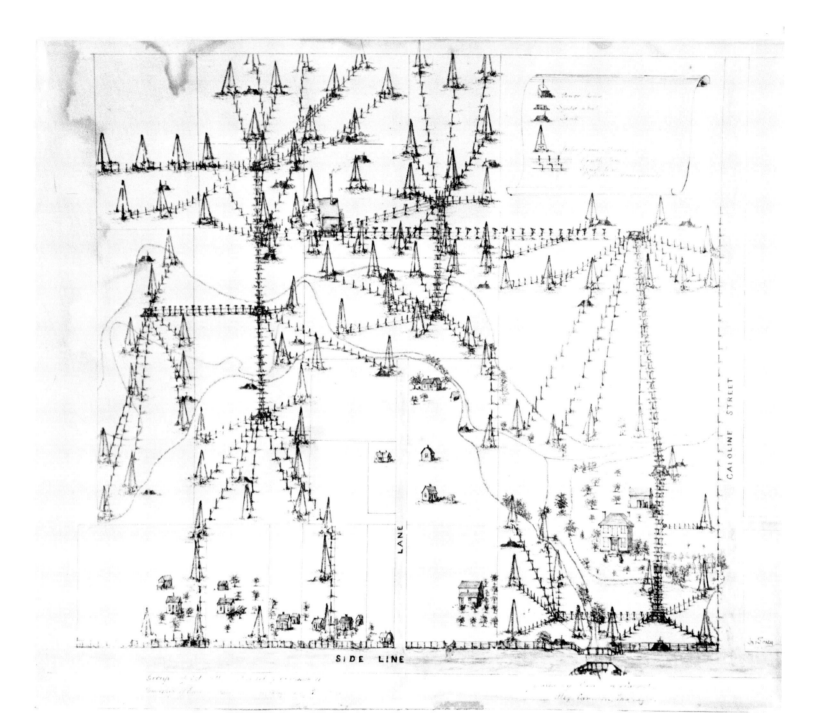

6-5   Oil wells operated by the jerker system, Petrolia, 24 January 1915. *National Archives of Canada* (PA-61253)

6-4   'Group of Oil Wells part of Lot 9 Concession 11 Township of Enniskillan [sic] . . . operated by Cameron & Calvert,' by John Tracy, c. 1870. *Courtesy of Mrs. John Stark and the Oil Museum of Canada*

6-6   Geared pumping rig, Oil Springs field, 1978.

6-7   Jerker system and field wheel, J.H. Fairbank Estate, Oil Springs, 1978. (The small building was originally a receiving station, built 1915, from which oil from local producers was pumped to railway tank cars on a nearby siding for shipping to Imperial Oil at Sarnia.)

6-8   Detail of 'spider' or field wheel.

6-9
Oil well, Oil Springs field, 1979.

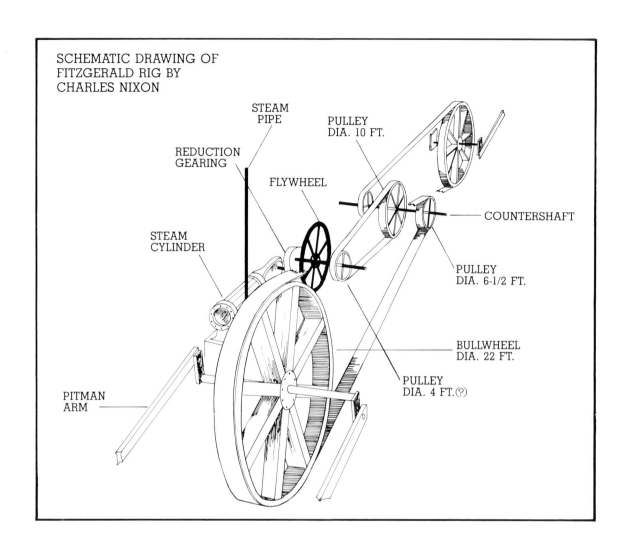

SCHEMATIC DRAWING OF
FITZGERALD RIG BY
CHARLES NIXON

STEAM
PIPE

PULLEY
DIA. 10 FT.

REDUCTION
GEARING

FLYWHEEL

COUNTERSHAFT

STEAM
CYLINDER

PULLEY
DIA. 6-1/2 FT.

BULLWHEEL
DIA. 22 FT.

PITMAN
ARM

PULLEY
DIA. 4 FT.(?)

6-11   Fitzgerald rig, Petrolia, c. 1903. *National Archives of Canada* (PA-96441)

6-12   Fitzgerald rig, Petrolia, 1903. *Toronto-Dominion Bank Archives*

6-13
Vertical eccentric pumping power,
Morningstar Oil Producers Ltd.,
Oil Springs, 1988.

6-14
Two wells, Morningstar Oil Producers
Ltd., Oil Springs, 1988.

7

London and Guelph Soap Works

The commercial production of soap from animal fats as a by-product of the meat packing industry began in the mid-nineteenth century. The adoption of continuous-processing machinery toward the end of the century led to greatly expanded production for both national and export markets. This, in turn, caused the establishment of a few large-scale vertically organized enterprises and led to the slow decline of the regional small-scale independent soap factories. The trend towards business concentration heightened in the 1930s with the introduction of fully automatic processing methods and chemical replacements for soaps. By 1980 less than a handful of the nineteenth-century soap manufacturing companies survived in Canada. The story of two of the oldest soap works, one in London, the other in Guelph, reveals how long-term survival was possible for a few of them.

Until the 1930s soap was made exclusively from a fat-alkali combination in a process known as saponification. North American pioneer families made thick and creamy 'soft soap' using cooking grease and leach from waste ashes. They made it once a year by the barrelful and retrieved it from the cellar by the crockful to do general duty as a laundry detergent, household cleaner, and toilet soap.[1] On a commercial scale, luxury toilet soaps were being produced in France before the nineteenth century. As described in the French encyclopedia by Denis Diderot in 1763, Marseille was the centre of the industry.[2] Here, soap factories produced batches of high-quality white soap from olive oil and lye. The soap-making process which Diderot describes was 'industrial' only in the sense that it took place in a factory (plate 7-1). After boiling, reboiling, and cooling for a day, workmen dipped the still liquid soap from the boilers by hand and transferred it to rectangular tanks where it hardened into great cakes. Workmen sliced these cakes horizontally with iron wires and vertically using a soap cleaver. It was Leblanc's discovery in 1790 of the process for producing soda ash from brine that paved the way for the large-scale manufacture of soap.

Small soap factories sprang up in most large villages and towns in North America by the beginning of the nineteenth century. As in France in the eighteenth century, the practice consisted of soap boiling over open fires, after which the soap was hand framed, dried, and cut. Throughout the nineteenth century and well into the twentieth, the batch method of soap boiling and framing continued to dominate in the industry. In the 1880s, however, the

1 Marilyn Mohr, *The Art of Soap Making* (Camden East, Ontario, 1979), pp. 78-80.
2 Charles Coulston Gillispie, ed., *A Diderot Pictorial Encyclopedia of Trades and Industry: Manufacturing and the Technical Arts in Plates Selected from 'L'Encylopédie, ou Dictionnaire Raisonné des Sciences, des Arts et des Metiers' of Denis Diderot*, Vol. II (New York, 1959), plates 472 to 474.

larger, well-capitalized enterprises introduced new high-volume steam-powered machinery for crushing, mixing, and drying. To compete, the smaller firms had to follow suit. Those that did not went out of business or were taken over by the larger firms.

Mechanical equipment for milling greatly expanded the commercial production of bar soap by the end of the century. The product was now lightly perfumed and coloured with natural essences and dyes which were made often by the soap master himself. Besides colours and fragrances, soap masters often added fillers, such as fuller's earth or silica (to produce a soft, silky lather suitable for baby soap), sand or fine pumice (for heavy-duty cleaning), milled grains such as bran or oatmeal (for an abrasive complexion soap), or paraffin and beeswax (to extend the soap and make it softer to the touch). They added natural emollients or superfats, such as vaseline, lanolin, fine vegetable oils (olive oil was the main ingredient in a hard, mottled soap called castile), or glycerine to hard tallow soap as softening agents. Glycerine soap had a special commercial appeal, since the public associated its transparency and clarity with purity. And finally, they sometimes added medicaments, usually disinfectants and antiseptics such as iodine, sulphur, camphor, and carbolic acid, to produce soaps for treating skin disorders in both humans and animals. Some specialty soaps — shaving soaps, for example — required a complex mixture of these scents, fillers, emollients, and medicaments.

Steam-powered machinery also was introduced in the 1890s for the large-scale manufacture of laundry and industrial soaps. The new machinery, which was greatly improved and automated in the 1920s and 1930s, guaranteed uniformity of size, thickness, and moisture content of soap chips and flakes produced as the base for later processing for laundry flakes, granulated soap, or toilet bars. The addition of electric motor drives in the 1920s eliminated the need for the old belt- and chain-drive systems of power transmission.

Expanded production and national advertising (soap was one of the first of the consumer products to be advertised under brand names) led to the rise in the 1880s and 1890s of large firms such as Procter & Gamble and Colgate & Company in the United States, Lever Brothers in Britain, and John Taylor & Company (Toronto) in Canada. The larger-scale producers created extended buying organizations to assure themselves of a steady supply of raw materials, such as animal and vegetable oils, fats, and soda ash.[3] These firms bought out

3 Alfred D. Chandler, Jr., *The Visible Hand: The Managerial Revolution in American Business* (Cambridge, Mass., 1977), p. 296.

many of their smaller competitors in the big merger movement in North America at the turn of the century. In Canada, soap production became increasingly concentrated in Toronto and Montreal. Not surprisingly, the large meat-packing and vegetable oil enterprises, such as Canada Packers and Swift Canadian, competed by producing soap from their by-products.

The dominance of the large capital-intensive corporations was guaranteed by the introduction of man-made detergents, called surfactants, in the 1930s. It was in 1933 that the Procter & Gamble Company introduced the first household synthetic detergent. The soapless detergents wash in much the same manner as soaps but are not based on the traditional fat-alkali combination. Most contain chemical components called 'builders', usually phosphate compounds which boost the washing power of detergents, and chemicals which whiten clothes and eliminate stains, protect washing machines against corrosion, and stabilize and suppress suds. A major advantage of synthetic detergents over soaps was that the former were effective in hard water. In the immediate post-war period, the quick-dissolving, fast-acting, pleasant-smelling, heavy-duty washing products virtually replaced the old soap-based flakes and powders. Today the synthetic detergents represent 85 percent of the total North American production and consumption.[4]

With the introduction of the soapless detergent in the 1930s, those independent soap manufacturers which had managed to survive had to concentrate on manufacturing luxury lines of toilet soaps for which regional markets continued to exist. A new important technique developed about 1940 was an extrusion process for producing bar soap in a continuous process — faster, more efficient, and with greater quality control than with the traditional method of soap framing, drying, and cutting. In the 1960s many soap manufacturers introduced entirely new lines of toilet soaps. These included deodorant and antibacterial soaps, 'beauty bars', and more recently, liquid bath and hand soaps which are a combination of soap and synthetic detergents. Besides producing new products, soap manufacturers used a new range of additives, including antitoxants, optical brighteners, stabilizers, and artificial colours and fragrances.

The trend in soap manufacturing since the introduction of soapless detergents has been to produce high levels of toxic waste caused both by the chemical effluents produced during the manufacturing process and also as a

4 Mohr, *The Art of Soap Making*, pp. 22-23.

result of the extensive commercial and household use of the new soaps and detergents. With increasing federal, provincial, and municipal environmental regulations, the disposal of chemical effluents became a major problem for the small soap manufacturer. The cost of equipment required to meet government regulations proved to be prohibitive for many of them.

The London Soap Company, 197 South Street, was the oldest operating, most intact soap factory in Canada when it was destroyed by fire in 1985 after an unsuccessful attempt by the city to preserve it as an operating industrial museum. The first soap business to be established at this location was an outgrowth of a tallow candle business started between 1871 and 1873 by William Starr.[5] (Before the introduction of kerosene for illumination purposes in the 1850s, candle-making was a common local enterprise in Ontario. The combination of soap and tallow candle manufacturing was natural, since animal fat was the main ingredient in both products.) During the next 25 years the soap-making operation on this site changed ownership at least four times. In 1881 it was identified as Thomas Churcher & Co., Steam Soap Works, Clarence Street. The firm advertised Churcher's Pure White Glycerine Soap 'for the nursery, bath, and fine linen', and Churcher's Premier Soap of Canada, 'a pale yellow soap, for general purposes'.[6] The soap works also became known throughout the region for its 'Home Sweet Home' laundry soap.[7] Not until 1887, however, was a soap works on this site listed in the city business directory as London Soap Co.[8]

Stability of ownership of the London Soap Company was achieved by 1912, when an experienced English soap-maker named Abner G. Phillips became proprietor. With him were Frank Phillips, shipper, and Harold Phillips, soap-maker. The Phillips family ran the business for the next 66 years, until 1978. A.G. Phillips had apprenticed in soap-making in England before immigrating to Canada. In Canada, he operated the Dominion Soap Works in Hamilton (John Taylor & Co. controlled it, then sold out to Lever Brothers in 1911),[9] after which he purchased the London Soap Co. A talented and enterprising man, Phillips quickly introduced many improvements and expanded the line of products to include industrial soaps, to meet the new demand created by the growing number of woollen and hosiery mills in the London area. About 1918 the Phillips family constructed a large addition to the rear of the original white

5 William E. Hitchins, 'The London Soap Company, 197 South Street, London, Ontario' (unpublished report to the Local Architectural Conservation Advisory Committee, 14 May 1981), London Public Library. Hitchins inventoried changes in ownership in the tax assessment records and city directory for the period 1854-1980. The London Soap Company site straddled Lots 6 and 7 on the south side of South Street west of Clarence, on the bank of the Thames.
6 Ibid., p. 3, Advertised in the *London Directory, 1881-82*, p. 23.
7 *London Free Press*, 28 May 1965.
8 *History of the County of Middlesex, Canada*. Original Edition, 1889 (Belleville, 1972), 889.
9 Mohr, *The Art of Soap Making*, p. 19-20.

brick, two-storey works, (plate 7-2), which had been expanded once before, in the 1890s.[10]

When photographed in 1979, London Soap had just been purchased from the Phillips family by a London businessman, Peter Soumalias, and his associates. Operating under the name London Soap & Cosmetic Co., the old South Street operation appeared to have a promising future. London Soap was a small-scale maker of low-grade soap products using local supplies of tallow and fat, and produced glycerine soap, specialty soap for health stores, and custom-wrapped soap for hotels and guest houses.

When the new owner took it over, London Soap was one of the last of the soap-boiling plants in Ontario, and it was proving impossible to find or keep a soap master (a problem also facing the Guelph Soap Company). Because so much capital is tied up in the raw materials which go into a batch of soap, the skills of a soap master are critical. The soap masters at both London Soap and Guelph Soap were about to retire. Apprentices, when they could be found, did not stay to the end of the year-long training period, in spite of the availability of various government funding programs to subsidize the apprentice's salary. The London Soap Company therefore abandoned the practice of soap boiling in favour of soap finishing using soap noodles. But all the equipment and machinery — indeed the plant itself — was outdated, and the owners wanted to modernize and expand the plant. By-laws, however, prevented expansion on the site, which was zoned as flood plain land. It was at this point that the idea was developed of a government-sponsored lease-back scheme in which soap-making would continue and the company maintain the building as an operating museum.

With its two generations of equipment, London Soap was already a museum. Saponification took place in three iron kettles, each approximately 20 feet in width and 30 feet in depth, one of which is shown in plate 7-3. There was an old-style soap-milling machine with granite rollers manufactured by Houchin-Aiken, Brooklyn, New York (plate 7-6), and a later version of the same machine, with five steel rollers, manufactured around 1915 by C.A. Crosby & Co. Ltd., Sarnia. The milling machines originally mixed soap chips with different fragrances before the production of hardened bars of toilet soap. The new generation of machinery included an automatic soap chip system supplied by Proctor & Schwartz and dating from the 1930s. Proctor &

10 Hitchins, 'The London Soap Company,' p. 6.

Schwartz Inc., Philadelphia, was a leading North American supplier of soap-making equipment. The company started up in the 1880s and quickly became the largest builders of drying machinery for dozens of industries, including soap manufacturing.[11] The first Proctor dryer for turning liquid soap into soap chips and flakes employed a five-roll chilling machine. Developed in 1898, it became the accepted standard throughout the industry. The firm continually improved its drying system, and by the late 1920s and early 1930s produced a soap dryer which had a much greater capacity per square foot of floor space, regulated the speed and uniformity of flow, and reduced steam consumption and total operating costs (plates 7-4 and 7-5).

Persuaded by the soap company's president, the Local Architectural Conservation Advisory Committee, and the Ontario Society for Industrial Archaeology to save the historic operation, the City of London and the Upper Thames River Conservation Authority jointly purchased the property, plant, and equipment in 1980 on a lease-back deal that committed the company to soap production at the site and public tours during which the historic equipment and procedures would be demonstrated. The purchase was part of a continuing program to buy flood plain properties in the city for conversion into park land. In December 1981 the city designated the soap works under the Ontario Heritage Act as having historic and architectural value. But there the concern for heritage ended. No one arranged for regular public tours of the soap works (indeed, the practicality of touring the public through such a dark and unsafe environment was highly questionable). No one undertook even to record the building or inventory and document the equipment.

Early in 1984 the president of the company abandoned the lease on the South Street factory after a two-year-old dispute with the city over its physical condition,[12] and consolidated operations at his other London plant. In response, the city launched a suit against the London Soap & Cosmetic Co. in September of that same year.[13] The issue was settled in the early morning hours of April 2, 1985, when a major fire destroyed the vacant works.

In a bizarre postscript to the story, the Ontario Society for Industrial Archaeology, helped by the City of London, Upper Thames River Conservation Authority, and the Ontario Ministry of Citizenship and Culture, erected a monument incorporating remnants of the C.A. Crosby & Co. soap-milling machine and three granite rollers belonging to the Houchin-Aiken milling

11 Proctor & Schwartz Company bulletins, such as 'Meeting the Demand for Thin Soap Chips,' (1927); 'Proctor Flake Soap System,' (1935); and 'The New Proctor Chip Soap System,' (1935), can be found in the Catalogue Library, National Museum of American History, Smithsonian Institution, Washington, D.C.
12 *London Free Press*, 30 April 1981, 7 June 1984.
13 Ibid., 12 September 1984.

machine to commemorate the old soap works. This curious memorial (plate 7-7) sits at the edge of an unlandscaped vacant lot in a quiet residential district where no one other than neighbours would have any reason to notice it. The monument certainly has not escaped the notice of local children, however; they have assembled small treasures — old tires, stones, broken glass, and bottle caps — on its thick concrete base.

Unlike London Soap, the old Guelph Soap Company is still in operation, and today is the oldest operating soap factory in the country. The Guelph Soap Company (Wellington Soap Works), started up c.1881 in an old limestone tannery located on Fountain Street and dating from the 1850s. A stone addition to the rear had been added by 1908, as shown in plate 7-8. Two additions, one of brick and, more recently, one of cement block construction, have completely changed the original appearance of the building. During the 1920s Guelph Soap turned out soap flakes under the 'None Ever Better' brand (plate 7-9) and a variety of toilet soaps. The business survived several changes of ownership until the depression decade of the 1930s, when it went into receivership. A family by the name of Harris acquired the business, renaming it the Wonderful Soap Company. Shortly after the purchase came the introduction of chemical replacements for soaps and the decline in business for small soap manufacturers such as Harris.

In a move which proved to be critical for the survival of this operation, a national meat-packing firm, Swift Premium Ltd., purchased the Wonderful Soap Company from the Harris family in 1947, renaming it Swift Chemical Specialties in the 1960s. Under Swift's management some of the old equipment was scrapped and replaced. In spite of the attempts to modernize this operation, the business proved ultimately unprofitable. This was in part because of environmental regulatory problems facing all urban soap works in the 1980s. After the City of Guelph rightly called a halt to the dumping of lye effluents produced at Swift Chemical, Swift Premium sold the business in 1983.

The new owner is Tricorp Chemical Specialties, headed by Martin Bosch, a former chemistry teacher with a keen sense of both business and history. Bosch immediately tackled the pressing problem of environmental pollution by adjusting his soap-making process to use up all the lye.

On the first floor of the original 1850s building sit five iron boiling kettles (plate 7-10). These kettles remain in use, not to make soap 'from scratch', but to process scraps (imperfect bars and soap noodles). Steam lines feed into the kettles and steam coils heat the soap to the required temperature. The other lines leading into the kettles once supplied tallow, water, and caustic soda. Although obsolete now that saponification of the tallow no longer occurs, the latter lines have been intentionally left in place as artifacts for visitors to see. The old tallow holding tanks remain in place in the basement below for the same reason. After being heated and mixed in the boiling kettles, the hot liquid soap is pumped upstairs, where it is converted into soap flakes using the Proctor automatic soap system dating from the 1930s (plate 7-11). Besides reprocessing scraps, Tricorp Chemicals purchases bulk liquid soap that by-passes the kettles, requiring the drying process only.

Today the old Guelph soap works are the basis of a highly successful operation. Tricorp supplies two leading national grocery chains with a complete line of brand soaps, and this year (1988) has begun producing its own soap bars under the name of the Guelph Soap Company Ltd. The company is also the producer of chemical additives for the concrete industry, a major distributor of lard oils in Canada, and the manufacturer of cleaners for the hardware trade.

Introducing new products required many changes to the old works. In 1987 the company built a large one-storey addition for storage and shipping, with a new company office fronting on Surrey Street. The heritage aspects of the plant are receiving equally serious attention. A brick and aluminum-siding shed has been removed to uncover one side of the old limestone building. This recently has been cleaned and the bricked-in windows reglazed to recapture the original appearance of the building (plate 7-12). Beyond that, the owner plans to eventually install a factory outlet and small museum on soap-making in the upper storey of the second oldest part of the works. All this is to be accomplished as an act of private initiative.

7-1   Soap boiling, with lye vats at left, from Denis Diderot, *Encylopédie ou Dictionnaire Raisonneé des Sciences, des Arts et des Metiers*, Plate Vol. 9, 1771. *Thomas Fisher Rare Book Library, University of Toronto*

7-2   London Soap Company, 1979.

7-3   Large soap kettle, with small iron steam-jacketted transfer kettle to melt large fats in foreground, London Soap Company, 1979.

7-4 'Proctor Chip or Flake Soap System,' from Proctor & Schwartz, *Bulletin* c. 1935.
National Museum of American History, Smithsonian Institution

7-5

Chill roller (part of Proctor Chip or Flake Soap System) to set the liquid soap before it is passed through the dryer, London Soap Company, 1979.

7-6
19th-century soap milling machine manufactured by Houchin-Aiken, Brooklyn, N.Y., London Soap Company, 1979.

7-7   Monument to the London Soap Company, 1987.

7-8   Guelph Soap Company, from the *Special Industrial Souvenir Number of Guelph Daily Mercury,* 1908.

7-9
Advertisement, from *Guelph Mercury
Centennial Edition,* 20 July 1927.

7-10
Soap kettles in the old section, Tri-corp Chemical Specialties, Guelph, 1988.

7-11
Proctor & Schwartz dryer powered
from line shafting, Tricorp Chemical
Specialties, Guelph, 1988.

7-12   Guelph Soap Company building (Tricorp Chemical Specialties) 1988.

8

The Whirlpool Rapids Bridge and its Predecessors

Few bridge sites in North America have as great historical and technical interest as that of the Whirlpool Rapids Bridge. It was here, in 1848, that the first bridge was built to span the Niagara River. The Canadian entrepreneur and politician William Hamilton Merritt and the American engineer Charles B. Stuart, who was involved with railroad surveys on both sides of the river, had initiated the scheme to build a combined railway and road bridge at a site where the gorge narrowed about 2 miles below the Falls.

The turbulent rapids, to say nothing of the enormous ice jams in winter, made it impossible to construct piers or falsework. The only structure that could be built at the time with a span long enough to bridge the 700-foot gorge without intermediate supports was a suspension bridge. Not only was the practicability of a railway suspension bridge doubtful, but the proposed bridge would have a span nearly twice that of the longest railway spans in the world at the time, the two 460-foot main spans of Robert Stephenson's Britannia Bridge across the Menai Strait separating Anglesey from the mainland of Wales. When a number of leading engineers were asked to submit their opinions on the Niagara project, only Charles Ellet, Jr., John Augustus Roebling, and two other engineers considered it feasible.[1]

Ellet and Roebling were the leading contenders for the contract to construct the bridge.[2] Ellet, the first American-born civil engineer to have had a European training, had built the first major wire-cable suspension bridge in North America, the Fairmount Bridge opened in 1842 over the Schuylkill at Philadelphia. Roebling, born and educated in Germany, had become the first major manufacturer of wire rope in North America. In 1845 his pioneering suspension aqueduct was opened over the Allegheny River at Pittsburgh, and the following year he completed a wire-cable suspension bridge across the Monongahela in the same city. In 1847 Ellet, again in competition with Roebling, was awarded the contract for his record-breaking span of 1,010 feet across the Ohio at Wheeling, West Virginia. This contract and Ellet's friendship with Stuart undoubtedly influenced the award, in November, of the contract at Niagara to Ellet, although his bid was higher.

Early in 1848 Ellet began the building of a temporary span with wooden towers. It was to be used as a service bridge during the construction of the permanent bridge. When the first cable had been secured, Ellet suspended a light iron carriage or basket from two iron pulleys to ferry men and materials

1 Charles B. Stuart, *Lives and Works of Civil and Military Engineers of America* (New York, 1871), p. 270. The other two engineers were Edward W. Serrell and Samuel Keefer; all four eventually built suspension bridges spanning the Niagara River.

2 In an early report on what it termed 'this interesting, and exceedingly important project', the *American Railroad Journal* referred to 'a spirited competition which will *of course* take place between the able and experienced engineers, *Mr. Ellet* and *Mr. John A. Roebling* — who have earned enduring laurels in the construction of wire suspension bridges in this country'. *American Railroad Journal* 19 (17 January 1846): 41.

across the river; the 'basket ferry' was also used to ferry more daring members of the public. The temporary bridge, the first to span the river, was completed in July 1848 (plate 8-1).

Work on the temporary bridge had hardly begun before there was friction between Ellet and the directors of the bridge companies, who found themselves having difficulty raising money for an expensive railway bridge to connect railroads that had not yet been built. Their relationship worsened when Ellet appropriated the tolls paid for the use of the basket ferry and later the bridge. The directors found him to be 'querulous, skilled in controversy, giving his whole mind to it'.[3] Their disputes did not end until Ellet resigned from the project at the end of the year.

In 1851 construction of the Great Western Railway of Canada finally began after several years of talk. This was to be a trunk line running from the Niagara River, via Hamilton, to Windsor, thereby connecting the lines that were shortly to be consolidated into the New York Central (1853) with the Michigan Central at Detroit. A railway bridge across the Niagara had now become a necessity; the contract for it was offered this time to John Augustus Roebling.

Ellet had planned to construct a single-deck bridge with a railroad track in the centre. It was to be supported by 'twenty cables of iron wire — 10 on each side'.[4] Roebling's design was very different. It was to be a double-deck bridge with the 'carriage and footway' 18 feet below the railway deck; deep wooden stiffening trusses connecting the two decks were designed to give the suspended structure the rigidity necessary to carry railroad traffic. Instead of 20 cables, Roebling's design called for only four, two supporting each deck. 'One large cable,' he wrote, 'does not only possess a much higher degree of stiffness, than a number of smaller ones in the aggregate, but the collective strength of the latter is even less than the undivided strength of the former, particularly when the structure is subject to motion and lateral vibrations, where the divided cables will never act in perfect unison.'[5]

More than any other engineer of his time, Roebling was concerned with dynamic stability and preventing the torsional undulations to which suspension bridges were subjected under very high winds. These had been the cause of the failure of many early European bridges, and on May 17, 1854, Ellet's bridge at Wheeling was almost completely destroyed by a storm. Roebling

3 Lot Clark to W.H. Merritt, 19 October 1848. Merritt Papers, Pkg. 35, Archives of Ontario.
4 *Niagara Falls International Bridge Company: Correspondence Relative to the Niagara Suspension Bridge* (Rochester, 1847), p. 6.
5 Ms. *Specification of the Niagara Bridge*, May 1847. Roebling Collection, Rensselaer Polytechnic Institute Archives.

considered it imperative to counteract the flexibility of a suspension span. He originally proposed to reinforce the stiffness of the superstructure by the use of 64 under- and over-deck wire-rope stays;[6] probably because of the disaster at Wheeling he increased this number. When completed, the bridge had 64 diagonal stays radiating from the bridge towers and 56 stays running from the lower floor to the rocks below[7] (plate 8-2).

Work began on the anchorages in September 1852. A nearly complete view of the system generally used by Roebling can be seen in the photograph, plate 8-3, taken in 1878 when the original anchorages were reinforced. Chains of iron links rose in a curve from cast-iron anchor plates. The looped ends of the cables were pinned to the upper ends of the chains, and the whole anchorage buried under a mass of masonry. The anchor plates, and all the castings for the bridge, were cast locally at the foundry of Oliver T. Macklem at Chippawa, on the Canadian side of the river.[8]

The towers and masonry were completed in November 1853, and the following month work started on the 10-inch cables, which carried the sets of wire-rope suspenders from which hung the two decks. These cables were built up from parallel wrought-iron wires 'spun' in position by travelling sheaves, a method devised and patented by Roebling. It was adopted by him for all his major works and was eventually used in the construction of every major suspension bridge until recently.

The first locomotive crossed the bridge on March 8, 1855. '*No vibrations whatever . . . ,*' Roebling recorded in his notebook, 'In fact less trembling than under the effects of some heavy teams on the lower floor.'[9] The success of the bridge was a triumph for the engineer, who was now recognized as being in the forefront of his profession. Roebling's last and greatest design was the Brooklyn Bridge, which he did not live to see. His right foot was crushed in an accident during the final survey for this bridge, and he died from tetanus on July 22, 1869, before construction began. The Railway Suspension Bridge, with its span of 821 feet, became, in the words of an 1857 guidebook, 'the greatest artificial curiosity in America'[10] (plate 8-4). While it established the suspension bridge as the coming type for long-span bridges beyond the reach of other types, Roebling's Niagara bridge was the only suspension bridge ever built for major railroad use.

In spite of its successful operation, the Niagara bridge remained the object

6 Ibid.
7 John A. Roebling, *Final Report . . . to the Presidents and Directors of the Niagara Falls Suspension and Niagara Falls International Bridge Companies*, May 1, 1855, second edition (Albion, N.Y., 1892), pp. 15-16.
8 Ibid., p. 20.
9 *Cables, Niagara, S.B. 1852*, Notebook 113, Roebling Collection, Rensselaer Polytechnic Institute Archives.
10 [John Disturnell], *Tourist's Guide to Niagara Falls, Lake Ontario and St. Lawrence River . . .* , (New York, 1857), p. 21.

of much criticism and predictions of disaster. In 1877 it was examined by several leading engineers. They found that the cables had become partially loosened from the concrete in which they were embedded at the anchorages, thereby admitting water which had rusted some of the outer wires; these were immediately cut out and new wires spliced in. The Great Western Railway, which held the lease on the upper deck, insisted on a further examination by a commission of engineers. This commission reported that the anchorages had to be reinforced, and recommended that the superstructure be renewed.[11] The engineer chosen to design and carry out the necessary alterations was Leffert Lefferts Buck.

Buck's greatest work was his massive Williamsburg Bridge, completed in 1903 across the East River between New York and Brooklyn, but, as David Plowden has written, 'his bailiwick was the Niagara'.[12] He not only made a series of major alterations to Roebling's bridge, but designed and supervised the construction of its eventual replacement, the Niagara Railway Arch or Lower Steel Arch Bridge, today known as the Whirlpool Rapids Bridge. He designed the rebuilding in 1888-89 of the Niagara Falls and Clifton or Upper Suspension Bridge. This bridge, constructed just below the falls by the Canadian engineer, Samuel Keefer, was opened in January 1869; its span of 1,268 feet made it the longest single span in the world until the opening of the Brooklyn Bridge fourteen years later. Buck again designed and supervised the construction of its replacement, his beautiful Falls View Bridge, completed in 1898. This bridge, which had a span of 840 feet between the bearing points of its two-hinged trussed arch, had the distinction of being the longest steel arch erected in the nineteenth century.[13]

Work began on the anchorages of the Railway Suspension Bridge in September 1877. The old chains were uncovered and new pits sunk in the rock at the back of each anchor wall. Chains anchored in these pits were attached to the strands of the cables on each side of the old chain. The additional chains increased the strength of the anchorages by about 50 percent.

The question of using steel arose during the planning of the renewal of the suspended wooden superstructure. Although Bessemer steel had been used for rails for more than ten years, the production and use of structural steel was very recent. The first bridge in America to have all-steel spans was then under construction by William Sooy Smith over the Missouri River at Glasgow,

11 Leffert L. Buck, *Report on the Renewal of Niagara Suspension Bridge*, 1880 (New York, 1881), pp. 11-14.
12 David Plowden, *Bridges: The Spans of North America* (New York, 1974), p. 179.
13 On January 27, 1938, after ample warning of a disaster, a huge ice jam in the gorge reached the level of the top of the skewbacks, which had been located near the water's edge. The arch was sheared at its hinges and collapsed with its superstructure onto the ice. It was replaced by the present Rainbow Bridge.

Missouri. Smith's bridge was completed in April 1879, about the same time that Washington Roebling made his decision to use steel for the superstructure of the Brooklyn Bridge. 'There appeared to be no doubt,' Buck wrote regarding the use of steel, 'as to its being the best material for many of the members of the bridge, provided that suitable shapes could be obtained, as its great strength would admit of decreasing the dead load of the bridge materially. But the use of steel has not yet reached a point at which all required shapes could be obtained economically.'[14] Buck 'decided to use steel for the posts, chords, track stringers and lateral rods. All other parts to be of iron.'[15] The contract for the furnishing of the steel and iron and the erection of the new superstructure was awarded to the Pittsburgh Bridge Company in May 1879, but it was not until April 1880 that work began at the bridge site. The replacement of the trusses and floors was completed without any interruption of traffic. Except for minor work, such as the building of sidewalks and handrails, construction was completed in September. The dead load of the bridge had now been decreased by considerably more than 100 tons.

The limestone towers carrying the four main cables had shown signs of disintegration for some years, but had been kept in fair condition by the replacement of defective stones from time to time. In spite of extensive refacing in 1883, cracks in the masonry continued to appear and were found to extend into the body of the towers. These cracks were partly due to the poor quality of the stone, but also to the bending stress on the towers caused by the failure of the cable saddles on top to adjust for the changes in temperature or live loads, such as passing trains, in order to maintain the equilibrium between the land and suspension cables. (The rollers under the saddles were eventually found to be immovably fixed in a mass of rust and cement.) In 1886 it was finally decided to replace the dangerously decaying towers. The substitution of iron towers outside of Roebling's stone towers without any interruption of traffic, except for a period of eight and a half hours when the cables were transferred by means of hydraulic jacks from the old to the new towers, was one of Buck's most remarkable achievements.[16] The work was afterwards described by Thomas C. Clarke and Charles Macdonald, two of the distinguished engineers who had examined the bridge in 1877, as 'the most daring feat of bridge erection ever performed anywhere or by anybody'.[17]

There now remained nothing of Roebling's original structure except the

14 Buck, *Report on the Renewal of Niagara Suspension Bridge*, p. 22.
15 Ibid., p. 24.
16 L.L. Buck, 'Replacing the Stone Towers of the Niagara Railway Suspension Bridge, with Iron Towers,' ASCE *Transactions* 17 (October 1887): 202-212.
17 *Engineering News* 30 (21 Sept. 1893): 236.

cables, suspenders, saddles and anchorages. The bridge had been given a new lease on life, but not for long. Ten years later the continually increasing weight of railroad traffic made it necessary to entirely replace the suspension bridge. Buck now designed a spandrel-braced steel arch with a span of 550 feet to be built on the same centre line as the suspension bridge, and constructed around it in such a way that there was no interference with traffic, which averaged one train about every 15 minutes. The contract for the superstructure was awarded to the Pennsylvania Steel Company. Richard S. Buck, who afterwards designed the suspension bridge built in 1899 connecting Queenston and Lewiston, was the resident engineer.[18] (The younger Buck was not a relative of L.L. Buck, but had been hired by him, apparently attracted by their same surnames, after the younger man had written to him when looking for a job after graduating from Rensselaer Polytechnic Institute in 1887.)

Ground was broken for the foundations of the arch span on April 9, 1896. Falsework was built out from near the top of the gorge to the water's edge for the erection of the end spans and the first panels of the arch. The two halves of the arch were then built out as cantilevers anchored to the solid rock on top of the bluff. Two travelling cranes, one on each arm, handled the steel members. To reduce the pull on the anchorages, the hoisting engines operating the tackle on the travellers were placed in the towers of the old bridge at the level of the railway floor. As the arch was completed panel by panel, the travellers moved forward on the top chords of the new structure. To give the massive double-track bridge greater rigidity, Buck had designed the arch as a two-hinged type with hinges at the skewbacks and no centre hinge. The absence of a centre pin made the closure of the arch more exacting, but it was successfully achieved after some difficulties.

The original negatives of a superb series of progress photographs of the construction are now in the National Museum of American History, Smithsonian Institution. These pictures vividly record every aspect of the extraordinary project from the construction of the skewbacks in the gorge to the dismantling of the cables of the old suspension bridge when the steel arch was completed (plates 8-5 to 8-7). The bridge was tested on July 29, 1897, under the load of 'two test trains as heavy as were available'.[19] Not a single train had been delayed during construction. The only suspension of traffic on the highway floor took place for about two hours each day when the upper floor carrying

18 R.S. Buck, 'The Niagara Railway Arch,' ASCE *Proceedings* 24 (April 1898): 263-288; 'The New 550-ft. Steel Arch Railway Bridge Over the Niagara Gorge,' *Engineering News* 37 (22 April 1897): 252-253.
19 R.S. Buck, 'The Niagara Railway Arch,' p. 287.

the new double track was being installed. All work on the bridge was completed on August 27, 1897.

Changes have been made to the decks and approaches of the now single-track bridge, but the steel superstructure remains unchanged today except for some additional bracing (plate 8-9). The Whirlpool Rapids Bridge is the only nineteenth-century bridge spanning the Niagara River that has survived essentially unaltered (the only other survivor from the last century, the International Bridge providing rail connection between Fort Erie and Buffalo, has an entirely new superstructure erected in this century). A writer in *Engineering News* in 1898 had indeed 'every reason to anticipate that the structure will be capable of serving the purpose, barring injury by corrosion, a hundred years from now as it is to-day.'[20]

20 *Engineering News* 39 (26 May 1898): 336.

8-1 'The Niagara Falls Suspension Bridge. First opened: Aug. 1st, 1848.' Lithograph by Wm. Endicott & Co.,
New York, 1849. *National Museum of American History, Smithsonian Institution*

8-2   Niagara Railway Suspension Bridge, from Emile Malézieux, *Traveaux Publics des États-Unis d'Amerique en 1870,* 1875. *National Museum of American History, Smithsonian Institution*

8-3
Renewing the anchorages of the Railway Suspension
Bridge, by George Barker, 1878. *Niagara Falls Public
Library (N.Y.)*

8-4 'The Great International Railway Suspension Bridge.' Engraving by D.L. Glover after a painting by Ferdinand Richardt, the bridge copied from a daguerreotype, 1859. *National Museum of American History, Smithsonian Institution*

8-5   Lowering stone for the skewbacks of the Niagara Falls Railway Arch (now Whirlpool Rapids) Bridge, 11 September 1896. *National Museum of American History, Smithsonian Institution*

8-6
View looking towards the American side, 23 February 1897. *National Museum of American History, Smithsonian Institution*

8-7
Dismantling the cables of the
Suspension Bridge, 2 June 1897.
National Museum of American
History, Smithsonian Institution

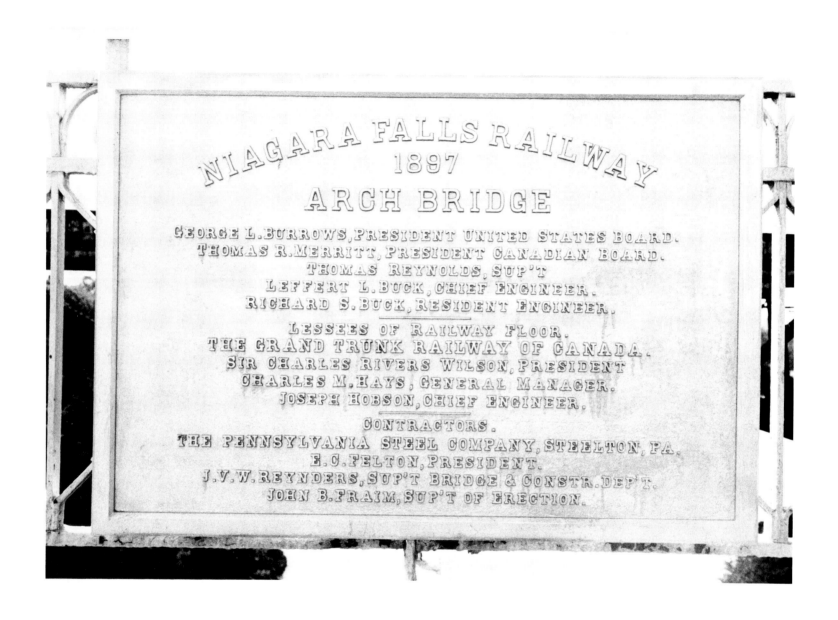

8-8   Name plate, Whirlpool Rapids Bridge, 1987.

8-9
Whirlpool Rapids Bridge, 1977.

8-10   Highway deck, Whirlpool Rapids Bridge, 1988.

9

The
St. Clair Tunnel

In the later decades of the nineteenth century the St. Clair and Detroit rivers became ever-growing bottlenecks for the railways connecting the Canadian and American sides of the busy waterway between lakes Huron and Erie. The heavy river traffic prohibited the building of multi-span swing bridges, while the flat countryside and low-lying river banks precluded the construction of high-level bridges with adequate clearance for shipping. The railways had to depend upon steam car ferries, with the ferry service often delayed by the many vessels passing up and down the waterway, and at times halted by fog and ice jams in winter.

In 1867 E.S. Chesbrough, who had engineered the first subaqueous tunnel in North America, the Chicago Lake Tunnel,[1] investigated the feasibility of a tunnel under the Detroit River for the Michigan Central Railroad. The intention was to improve interchange with the Great Western Railway of Canada, which via the Niagara Railway Suspension Bridge provided a direct connection with the New York Central Railroad. Work began in 1872 on a small drainage tunnel. However, the difficulties of excavation in the soft blue clay below the river bed, with sudden irruptions of sand and water, led to the abandonment of the project the following year, when the railroad's directors concluded that 'it would be throwing good money after bad to spend more upon the work.'[2] (It was not until the early years of the present century that the Michigan Central investigated anew the feasibility of a railroad tunnel connecting Detroit and Windsor. Construction of the tunnel itself was completed in 1909, with freight and passenger operation beginning the following year.)

The Grand Trunk Railway sent the bulk of its traffic across the St. Clair River near the outlet of Lake Huron, 60 miles north of Detroit. A car ferry at Point Edward, north of Sarnia, connected with the American lines that terminated opposite Point Edward at Port Huron, Michigan. By 1880 the Canadian railway had its own road from Port Huron to Chicago, the Chicago & Grand Trunk (today Grand Trunk Western), and was becoming a major trunk line for traffic from the Midwest to the Atlantic seaboard. The Grand Trunk decided to explore the practicability of a tunnel under the St. Clair, in spite of the earlier failure under the Detroit River and the probability that similar difficult soil conditions existed. In 1882 Walter Shanly, who had been general manager of the Grand Trunk from 1858 to 1862, and who with his

1 The Chicago Lake Tunnel, built 1864-66, extended two miles out into Lake Michigan to supply the city with clean water.
2 *Engineering News* 24 (4 October 1890): 292.

brother, Francis, had taken over and successfully completed the construction of the Hoosac Tunnel, the first major tunnelling work in the United States,[3] was asked to report on the project. Though he made no surveys or borings, he recommended a site between Sarnia and Port Huron, three miles south of the ferry crossing. Two years later, in 1884, officers of the Grand Trunk incorporated the St. Clair Frontier Tunnel Company and appointed Joseph Hobson chief engineer.[4]

Hobson was born in the Township of Guelph, Upper Canada, in 1834. After qualifying as a provincial land surveyor in 1855, he worked as an assistant engineer on the construction of various railways. In 1870 he became the resident engineer during the building of the Grand Trunk Railway's International Bridge spanning the Niagara River between Fort Erie and Buffalo, and in 1875 he was appointed chief engineer of the Great Western Railway. When the Grand Trunk absorbed the Great Western in 1882, it retained Hobson as chief engineer of the Great Western division. In 1896 he became the chief engineer of the Grand Trunk's entire system, a newly created position he retained until his retirement in 1907.

After careful surveys of the St. Clair River, Hobson decided to adopt the location recommended by Shanly. It is almost certainly no coincidence that the tunnel was to be in direct alignment with what was formerly the Great Western line via London and Wyoming, Ontario, and now the Grand Trunk's main line to Sarnia. The Canadian portal was to be located south of the town — today south of Confederation Street and west of Vidal Street in Sarnia's modern industrial section.

In 1885 test borings were made 50 feet south of the centre line of the proposed tunnel, so that the ground at the actual site would not be disturbed. It was found that the soil conditions were indeed very similar to those previously encountered at Detroit. Underneath the river bed of fine sand and gravel was a soft clay substratum approximately 40 feet in depth, permeated with water and overlying a loose, porous shale. In spite of these discouraging indications, the distinguished American engineer William Sooy Smith, who specialized in bridge construction and deep foundations, was engaged to drive a small exploratory tunnel or drift[5] with its crown about on a line with that of the proposed full-size tunnel. Work began with the sinking of small shafts at each bank. On the American side, the drift had advanced less than 20 feet

3 Work on the celebrated 4¾-mile railroad tunnel driven through Hoosac Mountain in northwestern Massachusetts began in 1852. In December 1868 the contract for the completion of the tunnel was awarded to the Shanlys, who finished their work in 1874. The Hoosac Tunnel was officially opened 1 July 1876.

4 In 1886 the Port Huron Tunnel Company was incorporated in the United States. The two tunnel companies were amalgamated in the same year as the St. Clair Tunnel Company, which in 1958 became part of the Canadian National Railway Company.

5 *Transactions of the Canadian Society of Civil Engineers* 4 (1890): 62-63.

when further progress became impossible in the wet, soft clay. On the Canadian side, in spite of the influx of water, quicksand, and natural gas, the pilot tunnel was driven for 186 feet below the river before all work had to be abandoned in July 1887.

Nothing further was done until the spring of 1888, when, with the continuing pressure of heavy traffic being ferried across the river, it was finally decided to begin work on the full-size tunnel. New borings were made directly on the centre line of the planned location. The work was made difficult 'by the number of vessels passing up and down the river and the general enmity of the boatmen to the enterprize, which could hardly have been greater if a bridge instead of a tunnel had been in contemplation.'[6] Several times the boring scow was struck and driven from its moorings. From the data obtained from the borings, it was decided to locate the tunnel, which would have an outside diameter of 21 feet, as near as possible in the middle of the belt of clay to avoid danger from gas trapped in the shale below. This left 'a layer of clay above and below the tunnel about 12 ft. thick on the average, although at one point the top of the tunnel is but 8 ft. below the top of the clay and the bottom of the tunnel approaches within 10 ft. of the rock'[7] (plate 9-1). Shafts were now sunk on each bank, but the almost fluid clay and silt rose in the shafts faster than it could be excavated. Again the work was abandoned and the shafts filled up.

In England at this time the City & Southwark (later South London) Railway, the first of London's 'tubes', was being engineered by James Henry Greathead — 'rightfully called', as Robert Vogel has written, 'the father of modern subaqueous tunneling'.[8] Greathead had built the second tunnel under the Thames, the small Tower Subway, in 1869. Here he had used a one-piece circular tunnelling shield of his own design and, for the first time in such a work, a lining of cast-iron segments. The tunnelling shield had originally been invented by Sir Marc Isambard Brunel for the driving of what is generally regarded as the first subaqueous tunnel in the world, the Thames Tunnel, completed in 1843. Brunel's shield was a massive rectangular cast-iron device within which the miners could excavate in soft ground ahead of the tunnel lining. Almost at the same time that Greathead constructed his Tower Subway, Alfred Ely Beach, the editor of *Scientific American*, built a short experimental tunnel under lower Broadway in New York City in an abortive

6 *Engineering News* 24 (4 October 1890): 293.
7 Ibid.
8 Robert M. Vogel, 'Tunnel Engineering — A Museum Treatment,' *United States National Museum Bulletin* 240, Paper 41 (1964): 218.

attempt to develop a passenger subway. To excavate his tunnel, Beach designed a circular tunnelling shield advanced by hydraulic rams instead of the propelling screws employed by Greathead and earlier by Brunel. Beach used a masonry lining in the straight section of the tunnel, but cast iron in the curved.

The failure of both the exploratory drift under the St. Clair and the first attempt to drive a full-size tunnel there showed that a shield was essential for such difficult soft-ground conditions, to support the face and ceiling in front of the lining and help prevent water and silt from breaking through and filling the workings. It was now decided to excavate open pits where the portals were to be located, and then begin excavation from both portals with the help of tunnelling shields. The tunnel was to be lined with cast iron. With the failure of all the preliminary work, the project had acquired a bad name with contractors. 'It was evident,' *Engineering News* reported, 'that even if a contractor could be secured who would undertake the work, he would have to be paid a very large sum above the actual cost to reimburse him for his risk.'[9] The company therefore decided to carry out the work itself.

To help in the design of the two tunnelling shields, Hobson attempted unsuccessfully to obtain working drawings of shields that had been used. His only guide proved to be Henry S. Drinker's classic book on tunnelling published in 1878 with small drawings of Greathead's shield for the Tower Subway and Beach's shield.[10] *Engineering News* described Hobson's design as resembling that of Beach's more than any other.[11] *Scientific American* not only referred to Hobson's shield as Beach's, but labelled its best illustration of it 'The Beach Hydraulic Tunnelling Shield' (plate 9-3).

The shield designed by Hobson consisted of a cylindrical shell 15 feet 3 inches long and 21 feet 6 inches external diameter, made up of steel plates 1 inch thick — almost three times the size of Beach's shield and twice that of Greathead's for the driving of the City and Southwark tube. The front edge was planed to form a cutting edge as in the shields of both Beach and Greathead, and like Beach's was advanced by hydraulic rams. Beach's shield, however, had neither diaphragm nor bulkhead, unlike Greathead's and Hobson's. In Hobson's shield the bulkhead of ½-inch reinforced steel was installed 4 feet from the rear edge. In the lower part of this bulkhead were two openings, 6 feet high and 4½ feet wide, through which the excavated material was passed. In the event of an inrush of water and silt, these openings could

9 *Engineering News* 24 (4 October 1890): 293.
10 Henry S. Drinker, *Tunneling, Explosive Compounds and Rock Drills* (New York, 1878).
11 *Engineering News* 24 (8 November 1890): 425.

be closed by doors suspended from chains above, but fortunately never had to be closed from the beginning of the work to the end. Three vertical and two horizontal partitions in front of the bulkhead strengthened the steel shell; the horizontal partitions also acted as platforms for the excavators. A feature of Hobson's shield was the 'segment hoist' mounted on a shaft at the centre and used to erect the cast-iron lining segments that weighed about half a ton. The Hamilton Tool & Bridge Works in Hamilton manufactured the two shields for the St. Clair excavation. Each shield weighed about 80 tons and was assembled at the site.

Work began on excavating the pits at both tunnel portals in January 1889. Tunnelling began on the American side in July, but a clay slide delayed the progress of the work on the Canadian side and tunnelling did not begin there until September. When the tunnel passed under the banks of the river, brick bulkheads containing air locks were built in the completed portions behind the shields, and the 2,318-foot section under the river was driven with the introduction of compressed air to maintain the working faces. This was not only one of the earliest uses of a tunnelling shield together with compressed air, but the first in which both the shield and pneumatic systems were used on so large a scale.

Hobson employed a pressure of only 10 pounds above atmospheric at first, but when the men struck bad ground, he increased this to 28 pounds. Cases of the bends were many, and three men died from the crippling disease when the pressure was highest. Almost at the start it was realized that the pressure was lowered too quickly when the men were 'locking out' of the compressed air. Smaller valves were installed in the air locks, but even then men after working in a pressure of 15 pounds would pass through the locks in about two minutes — a tenth of the time required at such a pressure today. The use of a single air lock in each bulkhead for both men and materials discouraged any lengthening of the short time spent in decompression.

From the time tunnelling began until the last lining ring was in place, the work went forward round the clock in three shifts, seven days a week. With the introduction of compressed air, tunnelling under the river progressed steadily with few problems. The tunnel was well ventilated, lit by electricity, and in spite of being driven through wet material, was kept quite dry — the cast-iron lining was almost perfectly watertight — by two portable pumps set just outside each air lock. Where the clay was fairly firm, a gang of about a dozen men would excavate for 2 to 3 feet in front of the shield; in very soft ground the shield was kept close to the working face or was forced into it. At times, in very soft ground, all the men would go back to the rear of the shield, which was then driven into the wet mass so that it filled the shield and came flowing back through the bulkhead doors, where labourers loaded the light narrow-gauge cars used to remove other excavated material. When a 20-foot seam of gravel was encountered near the Canadian side, the working face had to be plastered with clay to prevent all the compressed air from blowing out into the river. Even then 'there was an active geyser in the river over the tunnel until the gravel seam was passed.'[12]

When the shields came within 125 feet of each other, a small 6-foot drift was driven between them, and on August 25, 1890 Hobson, together with a director of the company and three other men, made the historic walk through from the American side to the Canadian side of the first major subaqueous tunnel in North America. The position of the shields was verified through this drift; when the two shields met five days later, their horizontal alignment was on virtually dead centre and the vertical only ¼ inch out (plate 9-5). The laying out of the line of the tunnel and the control of the alignment of the shields had been a major engineering feat in itself.

It had taken thirteen months to drive the 6,028-foot tunnel, and it was nearly another thirteen months before it was ready to be opened for traffic by Sir Henry Tyler, president of the Grand Trunk Railway, on September 19, 1891. The company did not let the contract for the excavation of the long approaches, which made the total length between summits about 2¼ miles, until tunnelling was almost finished and the success of the project assured. Now that the tunnelling shields had met, the partitions and bulkheads were cut away and the cast-iron lining completed; the shells of the shields were not removed but left in the clay, where they remain today. To protect the iron tunnel lining from corrosion caused by brine dripping from the refrigerator cars used in the railway's considerable traffic in frozen meat from Chicago, the lower half of the tunnel was lined with brick and cement and the upper half given a coat of asphalt paint. Track had to be laid, and pumping plants installed at both portals to keep the approaches free from water due to rain storms or melting snow, as well as pumps at the foot of the grade on the

12 *Engineering News* 27 (16 January 1892): 64.

Canadian side to drain the small amount of condensation and seepage collecting in the tunnel.

The Baldwin Locomotive Works, Philadelphia, built four specially designed decapod (0-10-0) locomotives with centre cabs for operating both freight and passenger trains through the tunnel (plate 9-7). The huge tank engines, the heaviest locomotives in the world at the time, weighed 195,000 pounds, all of which was carried on their 50-inch drivers for maximum traction on the 2 percent grade in the tunnel and its long approaches (the almost level section under the river was given a gradient of .1 percent descending towards the Canadian side to provide for drainage). The four engines burned anthracite to minimize smoke. Although two large Roots blowers were installed at each portal with a 2-foot air pipe extending to a point near the centre of the tunnel, the ventilation was reported by *Engineering News* in 1892 'to be so poor that the company is having difficulty in inducing brakemen to operate trains through it.'[13]

To prevent a break-in-two from stalling an entire train in a smoke-filled tunnel, trains were operated without air brakes. Tragedy occurred, however, when on November 28, 1897, the coupling broke between the first and second car of a heavy freight train as it was climbing the grade on the Canadian side of the tunnel. After leaving the first car in the Sarnia yards, the engine crew returned to the tunnel for the rest of the train, but were overcome by smoke and exhaust gases in a second attempt to have the train climb the grade. A rescue party was able to save the fireman and one brakeman, but found the engineer, conductor, and another brakeman dead.[14] A similar accident took place seven years later. On October 9, 1904, a train of 17 coal cars broke in two in the tunnel. The engine with three cars was run to the Sarnia yards, where the engineer uncoupled and then went back for the stalled cars. This time the engineer attempted unsuccessfully to push the 14 cars back and out of the American portal before he was overcome and asphyxiated, as were two conductors and a brakeman in the caboose. The fireman saved himself by jumping into the partly filled tank of the locomotive, where he remained for nearly two hours before being rescued in a serious condition. Two men of the rescue parties, the superintendent of terminals at Port Huron and a brakeman from Sarnia, lost their lives in attempts to reach the trapped train crew.[15]

13 Ibid. (12 May 1892): 487.
14 *Sarnia Observer*, 3 December 1897.
15 *The Railroad Gazette* 37 (14 October 1904): 451.

Before the second fatal accident occurred, the railway was investigating electrification, not only because of the danger from smoke and exhaust gases, but also to improve haulage capacity. The 2 percent grades in the single-track tunnel limited the weight of trains handled by the 0-10-0 locomotives to about 760 tons. Consequently, heavy freight trains arriving at the Sarnia and Port Huron terminals had to be divided into sections, which at times caused congestion in the yards as well as the necessary switching adding further complications to the train movements.[16]

The world's first main-line electrification had begun in the United States in 1895 at the Baltimore & Ohio's Howard Street Tunnel in Baltimore, with full electric operation there the following year. In spite of the success of the Baltimore electrification, it was several years before there were any more developments by North American steam railroads other than the electrification of several branch lines as a means of exploring the potential of electric operation. After a bad accident in a smoke-filled tunnel under Park Avenue, New York, in 1902, when fifteen commuters lost their lives, the New York State Legislature passed an act the following year prohibiting the use of steam locomotives in Manhattan after July 1, 1908. In 1904, when the Grand Trunk began its investigation of electrification, only the New York Central & Hudson River Railroad had progressed as far as contracting for its electrical equipment and motive power for New York; it was not until July 30, 1906, that the first electric train pulled out of Grand Central Station.

Bion J. Arnold, one of the distinguished electrical engineers on the New York Central's special commission to plan its electrification, acted as consulting engineer for the Grand Trunk's electrification of the St. Clair Tunnel, the first conversion of a railway tunnel in North America from steam to electric operation. Instead of using the General Electric Company's direct-current system adopted by both the B. & O. and the New York Central, the Grand Trunk decided to use the competing single-phase alternating-current system developed by the Westinghouse Electric & Manufacturing Company. The specifications, prepared by Arnold, stipulated that the locomotives 'should be capable of hauling a 1,000-ton train through the tunnel, from terminal to terminal, in 15 minutes, and at that in so doing the maximum speed should not exceed 25 miles per hour, and the minimum speed, when ascending a 2 percent grade, should be no less than 10 miles per hour'[17] (the

16 *The Railroad Age Gazette* 45 (6 November 1908): 1305.
17 Ibid. (13 December 1908): 1346.

steam locomotives at times could barely maintain 3 m.p.h. when hauling a heavy train up one of the grades). On January 4, 1906, Westinghouse was awarded the contract for the entire electrical system, which included the generating station built at Port Huron to supply power not only for the locomotives, but also for the drainage pumps and an extensive lighting system for the tunnel and railway yards and buildings at both terminals.

Westinghouse, with the Baldwin Locomotive Works, built six 6-wheel locomotive units with a 250 h.p. geared-traction motor connected to each axle. These locomotive units usually worked in pairs; a two-unit 'tunnel motor' was capable of hauling a 1,000-ton train at 11 to 12 m.p.h. up the 2 percent grades and could more than meet the specified performance (plate 9-10). All steam operation through the tunnel ended on May 17, 1908. Westinghouse, as the contractor, operated the equipment until it was formally taken over six months later by the St. Clair Tunnel Company on November 12.

Electrification brought many benefits, some perhaps unforeseen, such as the almost immediate increase in passenger traffic and reduced cleaning and painting of passenger cars as a result of the elimination of smoke and cinders in the tunnel. Locomotive maintenance and fuel costs were greatly reduced. In 1915 the *Electric Railway Journal* reported that the average cost per year for maintenance of the six electric units had been $11,131, as compared with $21,173 for the four steam locomotives they replaced, and the cost of slack coal for the generating station was less than half of that for the anthracite used by the four locomotives.[18] The company added three more electric locomotives to the roster over the years, but the pioneer tunnel motors remained in service until the end of electrification in 1958. In that year four diesel locomotives replaced the electric motors for handling freight; passenger trains now operated through the tunnel on their own motive power. The diesels assigned to the freight service were and are still known as the tunnel motors.

It was not until 1948-49 that any major change was made to the tunnel itself. After a consulting engineer had reported that the tunnel was structurally sound and that its life could be prolonged indefinitely with proper maintenance, the track was lowered to provide additional clearance to accommodate modern freight cars. Concrete stringers, to which the rails were attached with malleable iron chairs, replaced the timber stringers and old ties. However, these concrete stringers began to deteriorate with a few years, with the

18 *Electric Railway Journal* 46 (27 November 1915): 1085.

deterioration extending into the old brick lining on which they were laid; by 1972-73 the tunnel floor had to be completely reconstructed. New track was laid on short ties embedded in reinforced concrete.

When the tunnel was built, the height of a standard wooden boxcar was about 11 feet. Even with the additional clearance provided by the lowering of the track at the St. Clair Tunnel in the 1940s, the dimensions of the tunnel restrict today's steel freight cars to those no larger than the Association of American Railroads' classification 'plate C', which has a maximum height of 15 feet 6 inches. Nevertheless, about 15,000 cars are still handled every month by the diesel tunnel motors. In what almost seems like a return to the past, there is now a round-the-clock ferry service across the river for oversize cars (plate 9-14). Two tug/barge combinations ferry about 7,000 to 8,000 such cars a month. Both barges are cut-down car ferries; the *Scotia II* formerly plied the Strait of Canso, Nova Scotia, while the *St. Clair* ran on the Pere Marquette Railway's transfer across the river between Walkerville (Windsor) and Detroit. Some remaining evidence of the nineteenth-century car ferry operation between Point Edward and Port Huron can still be seen in the form of a dilapidated and abandoned station of unmistakable early Grand Trunk design on the American side.

Since the restricted clearance prohibits the movement of normal 'piggyback' service through the tunnel, Canadian National Railways introduced their 'laser' train in 1985. This is a unit train consisting of 12 specially designed low-deck articulated flatcars (plate 9-12). Each articulated flatcar can carry five semi-trailers. The special piggyback train operates at 'express' speeds — 60 m.p.h. in the United States and 65 m.p.h. in Canada — from Chicago to Toronto and Montreal, and enables the almost century-old international tunnel to be used in the movement of a modern intermodal freight operation.

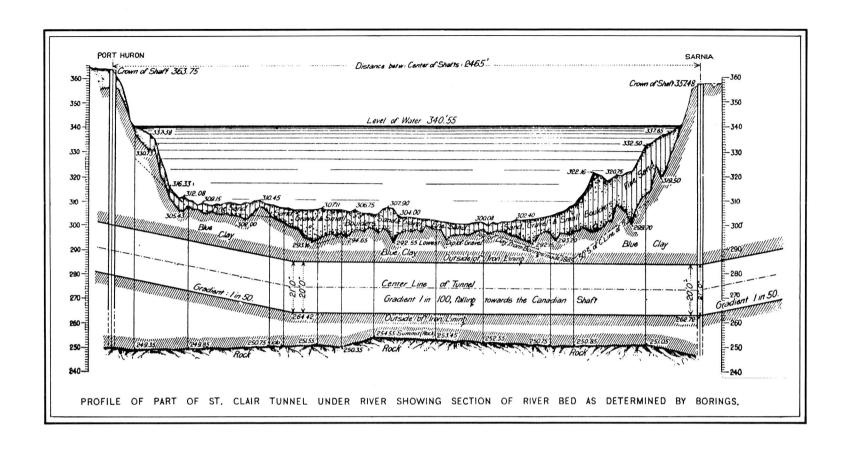

PROFILE OF PART OF ST. CLAIR TUNNEL UNDER RIVER SHOWING SECTION OF RIVER BED AS DETERMINED BY BORINGS.

9-1   From *Engineering News*, 4 October 1890. (The gradient falling towards the Canadian side is incorrectly shown as 1% instead of .1%. The scales indicate height in feet above sea level.)

9-2   Lowering one of the tunnelling shields after its assembly at the site, 1889. *Holland-Paisley collection, Sarnia*

9-3
The Hobson tunnelling shield, from *Scientific American*, 9 August 1890. *Metropolitan Toronto Library*

St Clair Tunnel Co

Sir we the persons whose signatures
wrote this requisition and who represent
the three gangs which dig in front of
the shield on the Canada side. being your employes
do hereby request that our wages be raised to twenty
five cents per hour. and eight hours a days work as usual
Our reasons for asking for this advance are 1st That our
work is under the ground away from the sunlight and
natural atmosphere ... ...
than any ordinary labourers this and the closeness of
the air around us make our days work a
continual succession of heats
3rd it is dangerous work in many ways
The effect of these disadvantages we find to be
very hard on our physical constitutions
breaking down many and making it
necessary for all to lay off frequently
to rest up and recuperate our health
Signed yours ...

John Chester
Charles Chester
Charles ...
John Moore
... Garcia
Richard Robinson
Geo Wells
Thos Jolly
...
James Bankes
... Smith

St Clair Tunnel Co.

Sirs we the persons whose signatures
encircle this requisition and who represent
the three gangs which dig in front of
the shield on the Canada side, being your employes
do hereby request that our wages be raised to twenty
five cents per hour, and eight hours a days work as usual
Our reasons for asking for this advance are 1st That our
work is under the ground away from the sunlight and
natural atmosphere 2nd The work is much more laborous
than any ordinary labour this and the closeness of
the air around us makes our days work a
continual succession of heats
3rd It is dangerous work in many ways
The effect of these disadvantages we find to be
very hard on our physical constitutions
breaking down many and making it
necessary for all to lay off frequently
to rest up and recuperate our health.
Signed yours Obt
Servants

9-4   Round robin requesting increase in wages. *Canadian National Railways*

Grand Trunk Railway

OF CANADA

Admit *J. A. Clement Esq.,*

TO THE

INAUGURAL TUNNEL BANQUET

AT

SARNIA, SATURDAY, 19TH SEPTEMBER, 1891,
AT 2 P.M.

THIS CARD WILL ALSO PASS THE BEARER BY THE
INAUGURAL TRAIN THROUGH THE TUNNEL.

L J Seargeant
Genl. Manager

9-6   Pass for the tunnel inauguration. *Ivan Harris*

9-5
'The meeting of the great
shields of the St. Clair
River railway tunnel',
from *Scientific American*,
13 September 1890.
*Metropolitan Toronto
Library*

9-7   Baldwin Locomotive Works photograph of 0-10-0 tunnel locomotive, 1891. (These
tank locomotives were eventually converted to tender engines, and still later given
conventional rear cabs.) *Railroad Museum of Pennsylvania (PHMC)*

9-8   The *Atlantic Express* exits from the Canadian portal, by W.E. Henry, June 1893. *National Archives of Canada* (PA-28818)

9-9   Maintenance crew at the Canadian portal, c. 1902. *Holland-Paisley Collection, Sarnia*

9-10   Electric locomotives with a block of refrigerator cars on the head end of an east-bound train, Port Huron, c. 1908. *Canadian National Railways*

9-11
Canadian portal, 1987.

9-12　　East-bound 'laser' train 238 exits from the Canadian portal, 1987.

9-13
Warning on Grand Trunk Western oversize
freight car.

9-14   The tug *Margaret Yorke* and barge *Scotia II* with oversize multi-level automobile carrier and Union Pacific high-cubic-capacity auto-parts car, Sarnia, 1987. (The tank car was not oversize but was transported by ferry for ease of switching.)

10

The Peterborough
Lift Lock

No engineering project in Canada has had a more protracted construction history that that of the Trent Canal connecting the Bay of Quinte on Lake Ontario with Georgian Bay on Lake Huron (plate 10-1). It began in 1833, a year after the opening of the Rideau Canal, with the building of a lock at Bobcaygeon to help local navigation. It was 71 years later that the most remarkable engineering project on the canalized waterway, the Peterborough Lift Lock, was officially opened. Although it was possible to make a through trip by 1920, with the completion of the conventional lock at Couchiching, it was not until the replacement of the marine railway at Swift Rapids by a modern lock in the 1960s, and the construction of a second and much larger marine railway at Big Chute in 1977, that the size of boats plying the canal was not severely limited.

In 1841 Hamilton H. Killaly, head of the Board of Works of the Province of Canada, submitted a very shrewd and farsighted criticism of the proposed 240-mile canalized waterway: 'The line of this intended water communication . . . with upwards of 820 feet of Lockage . . . continued through a series of lakes and currents, and in many cases extremely circuitous, is in my judgment quite unsuitable to the principal purpose for which it was originally recommended, namely, the line by which the produce of the Western States would be sent down to tide-water. The second argument advanced for its formation was the facility it would afford for the transport of the agricultural and other produce of the inland Townships to market; and thirdly, the advantages to be reaped by the Lumberers; the two latter I consider, can be obtained sufficiently, more immediately and at infinitely less cost, by the erection of two or three Locks to connect the long existing reaches of natural navigation . . . and, finally by the formation of [timber] Slides at the places where they may be required.'[1]

As Killaly had suggested, a few locks were constructed over the years to improve local navigation, and several dams and slides built by lumbermen. But it was not until a local outcry against the transfer of the works to the provincial government in 1878, at a time of economic depression, that any serious interest in the waterway was taken by federal politicians. The Conservative opposition led by Sir John A. Macdonald opposed the transfer and rescinded the order-in-council effecting it on their return to power the same year. New locks were constructed, but, after the Conservatives were reelected in 1887 with a :duced majority, they appointed a Royal Commission headed by A.C. Weller

1 Hamilton H. Killaly, 'Memoranda respecting various Public Works . . . ,' *Appendix to the First Volume of the Journals of the Legislative Assembly of the Province of Canada, Session 1841* (Kingston, 1842).

to investigate the advisability of proceeding with the project. The *Toronto Mail* commented: 'The authorities have from time to time expressed opinions and adopted measures which have led the residents of the Trent Valley district to believe that the Government seriously intends to build the canal. In the 1882 election this belief helped the Conservatives in Central Ontario counties; but in 1887 it was less potent, not because the Conservatives had altered their plans but because the Reform candidates professed to be as anxious as any person could be that, despite the expense, the canal should be built. In future contests the politicians in the district through which the projected work will run, will no doubt vie with each other in their pledges of devotion to the interests of the canal. The result will be that the work will be forced upon the party leaders, although it is almost a certainty that none of them approve of it.'[2]

The Weller Commission reported, perhaps not unexpectedly, in favour of continuing the works,[3] but it was not until 1894 that the government approved the construction of two new sections of the canal, including the one from Lakefield to Peterborough. To overcome the fall in the Otonabee River of 65 feet in a distance of about 800 feet at Peterborough, Richard B. Rogers, the superintending engineer of the Trent Canal, proposed the construction of a mechanical canal lift instead of the conventional flight of locks.

Rogers, who came from a Peterborough-area family and was an engineering graduate of McGill University, had elaborate plans for the waterway to become a major system of barge navigation. 'When the Trent Canal is completed,' he wrote, 'heavy freights can be carried from the upper lakes to the seaboard at less cost by the . . . cheaply propelled barges that are proposed for this canal than by any other proposed route.'[4] He suggested grain from the West could be transshipped at Midland from lake freighters to canal barges, which would then be 'towed by steam or electricity in fleets from five to ten in number'[5] to the ports of Montreal and Quebec. Rogers envisaged both electricity and compressed air being eventually developed on the canal itself as a source of motive power, but did not explain how he expected either power to be applied to the barges. He thought that hydraulic lift locks — essentially two huge boat chambers or caissons working in unison in a closed water hydraulic system — could alleviate much of the problem of the great amount of lockage required on the complex route.[6] These he estimated could raise a vessel 60 or 70 feet in the same time that it would take to navigate through an

2 *Toronto Mail*, 11 October 1887.
3 'Report of the Commissioners Appointed to Consider the Advisability of Extending the Trent Valley Canal, and to What Extent,' 17 December 1890. *Sessional Papers* No. 47, Session 1892, Vol. 25, No. 12.
4 Richard B. Rogers, 'Trent Canal,' *Transactions of the Canadian Society of Civil Engineers* 12, Part II (1899): 204.
5 Ibid.
6 The Weller Commission suggested the possible use of lift locks to reduce the time required for lockage, without the commissioners 'having formed any decided opinion upon it.' 'Report of the Commissioners,' p. 2.

ordinary lock of 6 to 7 feet.

The first hydraulic canal lift in the world had been constructed in England to allow boats to pass between the Trent & Mersey Canal and the River Weaver Navigation some 50 feet below. The Anderton lift, as completed in 1875, had two wrought-iron caissons large enough to take two canal narrow boats or one barge. Hydraulic rams supported the caissons in a balanced system connected by a transfer pipe. Removing 6 inches of water weighing more than 15 tons lightened the lower caisson; opening the control valve caused the heavier upper caisson to descend, causing the lower to rise. The Anderton lift had been designed by Edwin Clark of Clark, Stanfield & Clark, who supervised the construction of two more canal lifts, at Les Fontinettes in France, completed in 1887, and at La Louvière in Belgium, opened the following year. As at Anderton, these operated on the principle of a greater depth of water, or surcharge, in the upper caisson to set the rams in motion when the control valve was opened to begin the operating cycle.

No hydraulic lift had been built in North America when Rogers advocated the construction of hydraulic lifts on the Trent Canal. In February 1896 the Department of Railways & Canals sent him on a European trip to study the lift locks there before he prepared any specific plans. In Europe he contacted both the firm of English consulting engineers and the Belgian firm, the Société Anonyme de Jean Cockerill, which had built the French and Belgian hydraulic lifts. Although the design and construction of a lift lock both larger and higher than any of the three European ones was a major engineering project, only general specifications had been outlined when the Ottawa firm of Corry & Laverdure signed the contract for the excavation and concrete substructure and towers for the lift at Peterborough on May 7, 1896.[7]

It required an immense amount of labour to excavate the mainly hard clay and boulders 40 feet down to the limestone bedrock, which provided a firm foundation for the huge concrete substructure and towers. A steam shovel was used, but much of the work was done by hand. The press wells or pits for the hydraulic rams were excavated for 75 feet below the floor of the caisson pits into solid rock. Three courses of granite blocks, some weighing as much as 10 tons, were laid on the floor of each well to provide footings for the presses, and the wells were then lined with concrete. All the substructure, which includes the massive breast wall and wings that serve as retaining walls for the upper

7 Robert W. Passfield, 'The Peterborough Lift Lock, Peterborough, Ontario.' (Staff Report, Historic Sites and Monuments Board of Canada, Parks Canada, 1979), n.25.

reach, and the three guide towers, each 100 feet in height, were built of mass concrete (plate 10-2). It was one of the world's largest concrete structures at the time of its completion; more than 26,000 cubic yards of concrete was poured.[8] 'In order to avoid a bare look . . . as well as to obtain some architectural effects,'[9] pilasters, string courses, and cornices were formed in the concrete as the work progressed. Today some may object to these stylistic elements of traditional masonry construction, but the restrained use of features of classical stonework undoubtedly adds the dignity that was intended.

In spite of the magnitude of the project, the original contract with the construction firm of Corry & Laverdure required their work, which included the conventional locks at Ashburnham and Nassau Mills, to be completed by the fall of 1897. This was, to say the least, totally unrealistic. From the outset the lack of detailed plans and specifications, which were only provided as the work progressed, hampered the contractors. As late as October 1898 they had not seen the final drawings for the substructure at Peterborough and did not know the actual locations of the breast wall and towers. The specifications for the press wells were not completed until March 1899. There were many other problems, including bad weather which created a sea of mud at the construction site, and delays in the delivery of the cement supplied by the Department of Railways and Canals.[10] Rogers blamed the contractors for the slow progress of the work, but his own competence was, not surprisingly, called into question before the substructure and towers were finally completed in October 1902.

There were only two bidders in 1898 on the contract for the metal super-structure, the Société Cockerill and the Dominion Bridge Company of Montreal. The Belgian firm had expected to receive the contract because of their previous experience in the construction of European lifts, but the Canadian company was the successful underbidder. The company and canal staff had four years to perfect the design before construction began late in the fall of 1902. The basic plan followed that of the European lifts. An innovation was the installation of drop gates that were designed to lie flat when open in order to provide a headroom of 25 feet; the European lifts had vertical gates with a greatly restricted headroom. At the suggestion of the Dominion Bridge Company, the steel trusses of the caissons were given curved top and bottom chords, which provided both a more elegant design and greater strength than the original straight truss plan of Rogers. Although the huge rams were

8 It has often been stated to have been the world's largest concrete structure at the time, but at least one other structure, the San Mateo Dam, California, was considerably larger.
9 Walter J. Francis, 'Mechanical Canal Locks in Canada,' *Transactions of the Canadian Society of Civil Engineers* 20 (1906): 80. Francis began work on the Trent Canal in 1898 and the following year was appointed divisional engineer. He was responsible for the on-site supervision of the construction, and prepared the plans of the superstructure.
10 Nancy McMahon, 'Preliminary Construction History of the Peterborough Lift Lock, 1896-1904,' Parks Canada, Microfiche Report Series 139 (1983), pp. 24-34.

constructed of cast-iron cylinders bolted together (plate 10-3), cast-steel castings were used for the presses, also at the suggestion of the contractors. By November 1903 the work was completed.

An important postscript to the story has to do with Rogers himself. At the official opening, which took place on July 9, 1904 (plate 10-6), all the dignitaries present praised the work of Rogers, who during the long construction had been subjected to much criticism. His problems, however, were not over. A year later the *Peterborough Examiner* charged that a dangerous leak had developed in the upper reach of the lock and demanded an official investigation.[11] Henry Holgate, an Ottawa consulting engineer, was appointed to carry out the inquiry which Rogers himself requested in the expectation of being absolved of all charges of incompetence in either the design and planning or the supervision of the construction. Holgate, however, reported that there were problems with both the planning and construction, and furthermore that it could not be shown that a lift lock was 'best suited to the requirements of the Canal'.[12] He criticized the hydraulic lift as being expensive both to construct and maintain. A copy of Holgate's report was sent to Rogers, who resigned as requested from his position as superintending engineer in March 1906.

Rogers felt that he had been badly treated and was the object of political malice. When a Conservative government replaced the Liberal one in 1911, he pressed for a new inquiry. The original investigation was eventually reviewed by Charles H. Keefer, a Canadian member of the American Society for Civil Engineers. He virtually exonerated Rogers. Keefer considered hydraulic lift locks 'admirably adapted' for the canal, though he admitted they were expensive. 'If, however, a large traffic develops on the Trent Canal,' he wrote, 'their adoption would, I am sure, be amply justified in the saving of time and water.'[13] Rogers was temporarily appeased, only to find to his anger that he had to pay for the costs of Keefer's inquiry. As he wrote to the Minister of Railways and Canals, 'An official vindication at the private expense of the person vindicated forms a precedent that does little credit to the administration.'[14]

The leakage in the upper reach was neither serious nor the fault of Rogers, and it was easily remedied. In fact, the lift lock worked flawlessly for almost twenty years before a leak developed in the air compressor system that inflated the rubber tube seals between the ends of the caissons and the canal reaches,

11 *Peterborough Examiner*, 5 December 1905.
12 Charles H. Keefer, *A Review . . . on the Construction of the Hydraulic Lift Locks . . . .* (Peterborough, n.d.), p. 7.
13 Ibid., p. 8.
14 Quoted in Nancy McMahon, 'Preliminary Construction History,' p. 75.

and operated the pump for keeping the caisson pits dry. Although the leak was repaired, the original compressor system was replaced in 1926.

When the Peterborough Lift Lock was first opened in 1904, the extra depth of water or surcharge required to operate was obtained by stopping the ascending caisson 8¼ inches below the floor of the upper reach. The extra depth of water then entering the caisson provided an additional weight of about 100 tons on the supporting ram. When the main gate valve of the 12-inch pipe connecting the two presses was opened, the heavier upper caisson descended, forcing water from the press below it into the other press under a pressure of 600 p.s.i. and thereby driving the ram of the lower caisson upwards (plate 10-5).

Only three men were needed to operate the lock. Two gatemen, one at the lower level and one at the upper, took charge of the boats at about 200 feet on either side of the lock. They opened and closed the gates, inflated or deflated the rubber tube seals, and operated the hydraulic capstans used to tow vessels in and out of the caissons. The lockmaster, in his cabin on top of the centre tower, directed the two gatemen by a simple signal system and controlled the main valve between the presses. An interlocking system ensured that the entire operation was carried out in the proper sequence. It took from 12 to 15 minutes to pass one or two boats through the lock, with the elevation of one caisson and simultaneous descent of the other taking about two to three minutes of that time.

In 1900 excavation began for a second hydraulic lift lock, similar in operation, near the village of Kirkfield on the stretch of canal between Balsam Lake and Lake Simcoe. The major difference in the design was the use of trussed steelwork for the three guide towers instead of concrete. The huge caissons, each 140 feet long, 33 feet wide, and carrying 8 feet of water on the sills, are virtually identical to those at Peterborough. The contract for the steelwork was again awarded to the Dominion Bridge Company. The Kirkfield lock, which has a lift of 49 feet, was opened on July 6, 1907.

The completion of the two lift locks opened a 145-mile section of the canal to navigation between Lake Simcoe and Healey Falls. It was to be another thirteen years before boats, restricted in size by the small marine railways at Big Chute and Swift Rapids,[15] could pass through the entire system from Georgian Bay to Lake Ontario. In the meantime, the capacity of both the

15 The marine railways restricted the size of vessels to 60 feet by 13½ feet with a 4½-foot draft.

Great Lakes steamers and the railways for the transport of grain from the West had been vastly increased since the turn of the century, when difficulties with the movement of millions of bushels of Canadian wheat had given some specious logic to the idea that the Trent Canal could become an important system of barge navigation as envisaged by Rogers. The heavy commercial traffic which would have justified the construction of the lift locks never developed, and the canal eventually became the solely recreational waterway it is today.

In the 1960s the federal Department of Transport undertook a major modernization of the Trent Canal. This included changes to both the Peterborough and Kirkfield locks. At Peterborough they replaced the steel gates with aluminum ones, similarly hinged on the bottom but with a new sealing system, and now controlled from a new control cabin erected on the centre pier of the upper canal reach. Other changes in 1963-64 included the replacement of almost all the auxiliary machinery so that the lock, 'which had been built to operate almost automatically and independent of any outside power source, was now made dependent for the new auxiliary equipment on an oil hydraulic system with pumps driven by electric motors.'[16] In spite of these changes, the appearance of the Peterborough Lift Lock was little altered except for the addition of the new control cabin (plates 10-7 and 10-8). New hydraulic and electrical systems were similarly installed at Kirkfield, where the removal of the operator's cabin crowning the steelwork and the rebuilding in concrete of the steel aqueduct over the road have resulted in greater changes in its appearance (plate 10-10).

The administration of the Trent Canal was transferred in 1972 to Parks Canada. Now known as the Trent-Severn Waterway, the canal is today the busiest of Canada's recreational 'heritage canals'. In 1987 more than 6,500 boats locked through the Peterborough lift, still the highest *hydraulic* lift lock in the world and an impressive monument to both engineering skill and the power of politics.

16 Robert W. Passfield, 'The Lift Lock Then and Now,' in *The Peterborough Hydraulic Lift Lock*, ed. by Jean Murray Cole (Peterborough, 1987), p. 39. This excellent historical booklet published by the Friends of the Trent-Severn Waterway contains a detailed description of the original engineering and later changes.

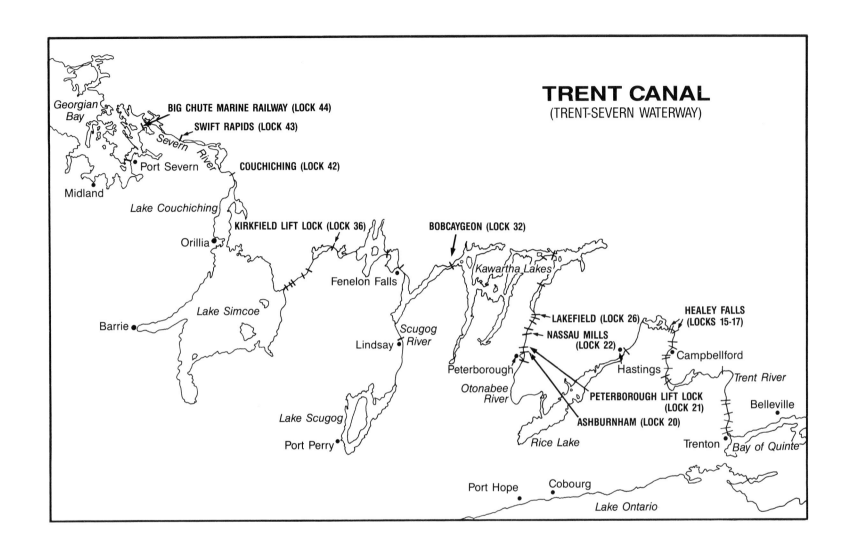

TRENT CANAL
(TRENT-SEVERN WATERWAY)

Georgian Bay

BIG CHUTE MARINE RAILWAY (LOCK 44)

SWIFT RAPIDS (LOCK 43)

Severn River

Port Severn

COUCHICHING (LOCK 42)

Midland

Lake Couchiching

KIRKFIELD LIFT LOCK (LOCK 36)

BOBCAYGEON (LOCK 32)

Orillia

Kawartha Lakes

Fenelon Falls

Lake Simcoe

LAKEFIELD (LOCK 26)

HEALEY FALLS (LOCKS 15-17)

Barrie

Scugog River

NASSAU MILLS (LOCK 22)

Lindsay

Campbellford

Peterborough

Hastings

Trent River

Otonabee River

PETERBOROUGH LIFT LOCK (LOCK 21)

Belleville

Lake Scugog

ASHBURNHAM (LOCK 20)

Port Perry

Rice Lake

Trenton

Bay of Quinte

Port Hope

Cobourg

Lake Ontario

10-1   Map by Paula Cameron.

10-2
The east tower under construction, 10 May
1902. *Trent-Severn Waterway, Parks Canada*

10-3   Work crew posed during the assembly of the east ram, 1 December 1902. *Trent-Severn Waterway, Parks Canada*

826

10-4   General view of the works, 13 June 1903. *Trent-Severn Waterway, Parks Canada*

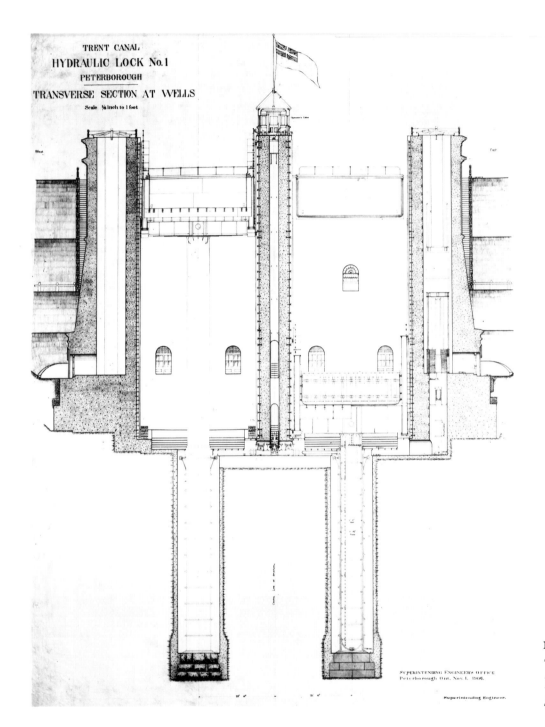

TRENT CANAL
HYDRAULIC LOCK No.1
PETERBOROUGH

TRANSVERSE SECTION AT WELLS

Scale ⅛ inch to 1 foot

SUPERINTENDING ENGINEER'S OFFICE
Peterborough Ont. Nov. 1, 1906.

Superintending Engineer.

10-5

Transverse section, by the Superintending
Engineer's Office, 1 November 1906. *Trent-
Severn Waterway, Parks Canada*

10-6   Opening day, 9 July 1904. *National Archives of Canada* (PA-138902)

10-7   The breastwall from Hunter Street, 1987.

10-8
General view, 1987.

10-9
View between the caissons during the construction of the Kirkfield Lift Lock, c. 1906- 07.
Trent-Severn Waterway, Parks Canada

10-10 Kirkfield Lift Lock, 1987.

Selected Bibliography of Secondary Works

1. *Topics Related to the Essays*

Binney, Marcus, and David Pearce, eds. *Railway Architecture*. New York: Van Nostrand Reinhold Co., 1979. Written by members of Save Britain's Heritage.

Brantly, J.E. *History of Oil Well Drilling*. Houston: Gulf Publishing, 1971. A poorly edited but unique reference work with details of the 'Canadian system' of drilling.

Brown, Kenneth, and J.T. van Riemsdijk. *The Pictorial History of Steam Power*. London: Octopus Books, 1980. Its popular format belies its excellence as a reference work.

Built in the U.S.A.: American Buildings from Airports to Zoos. Washington, D.C.: U.S. National Trust for Historic Preservation, 1985. Illustrated capsule accounts by authorities on such topics as railroad stations, breweries, bridges, and industrial structures.

Bush, Edward Forbes. *Commercial Navigation on the Rideau Canal*, 1832-1961. *History and Archaeology* 54. Ottawa: Parks Canada, 1981.

Cole, Jean Murray, ed. *The Peterborough Hydraulic Lift Lock*. Peterborough: Friends of the Trent-Severn Waterway, 1987. A collection of essays; excellent for details.

Condit, Carl W. *American Building Art in the Nineteenth Century*. New York: Oxford University Press, 1960. A major survey of civil engineering in the United States, which includes the international bridges at Niagara. Regrettably inaccurate in important details.

Dean, W.G., ed. *Economic Atlas of Ontario*. Toronto: University of Toronto Press, 1969.

Downward, William L. *Dictionary of the History of the American Brewing and Distilling Industries*. Westport, Conn.: Greenwood Press, 1980. More on the former than the latter, but an indispensable reference work nonetheless.

Drummond, Ian M. *Progress Without Planning: The Economic History of Ontario from Confederation to the Second World War*. Ontario Historical Studies Series for the Government of Ontario. Toronto: University of Toronto Press, 1987. Separate essays by Drummond and others on topics such as electrification, oil and gas, manufacturing, the iron and steel industry, and Ontario's 'industrial revolution'.

Fram, Mark. *Ontario Hydro: Ontario Heritage: A Study of Strategies for the Conservation of the Heritage of Ontario Hydro*. Heritage Planning Studies Series No. 4. Toronto: Historical Planning and Research Branch, Ontario Ministry of Culture and Recreation, 1980. Omits discussion of privately owned plants in the Ontario Hydro grid, such as those owned by Gananoque Light & Power Ltd. along the Rideau Canal.

Greenhill, Ralph. *Engineer's Witness*. Toronto and Boston: The Coach House Press and David R. Godine, Publisher, 1985. Nineteenth-century photographs of civil and mechanical engineering in North America.

———. *Spanning Niagara: The International Bridges 1848-1962*. Exhibition catalogue. Niagara Falls, N.Y.: Niagara University, 1984.

Hunter, Louis C. *A History of Industrial Power in the United States, 1780-1930*. Vol. 1. *Waterpower in the Century of the Steam Engine*. Charlottesville: University of Virginia Press, 1985.

———. *A History of Industrial Power in the United States, 1780-1930*. Vol. 2. *Steam Power*. Charlottesville: University of Virginia Press, 1985.

James, William, and Evelyn M. James. *'A Sufficient Quantity of Pure and Wholesome Water': The Story of Hamilton's Old Pumphouse*. London, Ont.: ?, 1978. An unstructured work of local history.

Legget, Robert F. 'The Jones Falls Dam on the Rideau Canal, Ontario, Canada.' *Transactions of the Newcomen Society* 31 (1959): 205-18.

———. *Rideau Waterway*, second edition. Toronto: University of Toronto Press, 1986. A combined tourist guide and history which pays little attention to 20th-century developments.

Middleton, William D. *When the Steam Railroads Electrified*. Milwaukee: Kalmbach Books, 1974.

Mohr, Marilyn. *The Art of Soap Making*. A Harrowsmith Primer. Camden East, Ont.: Camden House Publishing Ltd., 1979. Good layman's guide to the history and techniques of this industry.

Newell, Dianne. 'Technological Innovation and Persistence in the Ontario Oilfields: Some Evidence from Industrial Archaeology.' *World Archaeology* 15, 2 (1983): 184-95.

———. *Technology on the Frontier: Mining in Old Ontario*. Vancouver: University of British Columbia Press, 1986.

Passfield, Robert W. *Building the Rideau Canal: A Pictorial History*. Don Mills, Ont.: Fitzhenry & Whiteside, with Parks Canada, 1982.

Plowden, David. *Bridges: The Spans of North America*. New York: The Viking Press, 1974. A superbly illustrated book with much Canadian content, but unfortunately with inaccuracies.

Ritchie, T. *Canada Builds 1867-1967*. Toronto: The University of Toronto Press, 1967.

Sandström, Gösta E. *The History of Tunnelling: Underground Workings Through the Ages*. London: Barrie & Rockcliff, 1963. While international in scope, there is no mention of the St. Clair Tunnel project.

Shuttleworth, E.B. *The Windmill and its Times: A Series of Articles dealing with the Early Days of the [Gooderham and Worts] Windmill*. Toronto, 1924.

Williamson, Harold F., and Arnold R. Daum. *The American Petroleum Industry: The Age of Illumination 1859-1899*. Evanston, Ill.: Northwestern University Press, 1959.

————, Ralph L. Adreano, Arnold R. Daum, and Gilbert C. Klose. *The American Petroleum Industry: The Age of Energy 1899-1959*. Evanston, Ill.: Northwestern University Press, 1963.

2. Industrial Archaeology

Bloomfield, G.T. 'Canadian Fire Insurance Plans and Industrial Archeology.' *IA: The Journal of the Society for Industrial Archeology* 8, 1 (1982): 76-80.

Carter, Margaret. *Researching Heritage Buildings*. Ottawa: Parks Canada, 1983.

Cossons, Neil. *The BP Book of Industrial Archaeology*. Newton Abbot: David & Charles, 1975. Excellent introduction to specific topics.

Hudson, Kenneth. *The Archaeology of Industry*. New York: Charles Scribner's Sons, 1976. A plainly written introduction to the subject, it focuses on mining and quarrying, metal-processing and engineering, manufacturing and transport, and the food and beverage industries in several countries. Includes a brief section on the Rideau Canal.

Kemp, Emory L., and Theodore Anton Sande, eds. *Historic Preservation of Engineering Works*. Conference proceedings. New York: American Society of Civil Engineers, 1981.

Kidney, Walter C. *Working Places: The Adaptive Use of Industrial Buildings*. Pittsburgh: Ober Park Associates, Inc., with the Society for Industrial Archeology, 1976. A useful handbook showing that industrial buildings are valuable resources in American communities and can serve a broad range of uses.

Major, J.K. *Fieldwork in Industrial Archaeology*. London, 1975.

McKee, Harley J., Comp. *Recording Historic Buildings*. Washington, D.C.: Historic American Building Survey, U.S. Parks Service, 1970. Contains a section on recording industrial and engineering structures.

Newell, Dianne. 'Industrial Archaeology.' In *The Canadian Encyclopedia*. Vol. 1. Edmonton: Hurtig, 1985, p. 74.

Pannell, J.P.M. *The Techniques of Industrial Archaeology*. Newton Abbot: David & Charles, 1974. A good guide to fieldwork.

Vogel, Robert M. 'Quadrangular Treasure: The Cartographic Route to Industrial Archeology.' *IA: The Journal of the Society for Industrial Archeology* 6, 1 (1980): 25-54.

——, ed. *A Report on the Mohawk-Hudson Area Survey: A Selective Recording of the Industrial Archeology of the Mohawk and Hudson River Valleys in the Vicinity of Troy, N.Y.* Washington, D.C.: Smithsonian Institution, 1972. A model report of a pioneering project in the field.

Weiler, John. *Our Working Past: Conserving Industrial Relics for Recreation and Tourism*. Toronto: The Author, 1982. It is the only general work of its kind with a mostly Canadian content.

The italicized figures refer to plate numbers. A footnote is referred to by the letter n.

Published by:
THE BOSTON MILLS PRESS
132 Main Street
Erin, Ontario NoB 1To
(519) 833-2407 Fax: (519) 833-2195

American Association
for State and Local History
Award of Merit

Winners of the
Heritage Canada
Communications Award

Design by Gillian Stead
Typography by Lexigraf, Tottenham
Printing by Ampersand, Guelph

We wish to acknowledge the financial assistance and encouragement of The
Canada Council, the Ontario Arts Council and the Office of the
Secretary of State.